ATE DUE

'5 Aug '72

DATE DUE

AUG 1987	JUL 24 1987 RET	
SEP 15 1992 BIRD		SEP 3 0 1992

Demco, Inc. 38-293

The Transfer of Technology to Developing Countries

PARTICIPANTS AT THE AIRLIE HOUSE CONFERENCE
ON TRANSFER OF TECHNOLOGY

JOHN H. ADLER, Director, Economic Development Institute, World Bank, Washington, D.C.

JACK BARANSON, World Bank, Washington, D.C.

NEIL W. CHAMBERLAIN, Department of Economics, Yale University, New Haven, Conn.

C. E. FERGUSON, Department of Economics and Business Administration, Duke University, Durham, N.C.

ALEXANDER GERSCHENKRON, Department of Economics, Harvard University, Cambridge, Mass.

BERT F. HOSELITZ, Department of Economics, The University of Chicago, Chicago, Ill.

CHARLES E. HUTCHINSON, Chief, Behavioral Science Division, U. S. Air Force Office of Scientific Research, Washington, D.C.

JOHN W. KENDRICK, Department of Economics, University of Connecticut, Storrs, Conn.

JAN KMENTA, Department of Economics, Michigan State University, East Lansing, Mich.

SERGE-CHRISTOPHE KOLM, Economics Research Project, Harvard University, Cambridge, Mass.

MELVIN KRANZBERG, Editor-in-Chief, *Technology and Culture*, Case Institute of Technology, Cleveland, O.

KELVIN J. LANCASTER, Department of Economics, Johns Hopkins University, Baltimore, Md.

FRITZ KARL MANN, Department of Economics, University of Cologne, and Department of Economics, American University, Washington, D.C.

EDWIN MANSFIELD, Wharton School of Finance and Commerce, University of Pennsylvania, Philadelphia, Pa.

RICHARD L. MEIER, School of Natural Resources, University of Michigan, Ann Arbor, Mich.

JOHN JOSEPH MURPHY, Department of Economics, Catholic University of America, Washington, D.C.

RICHARD R. NELSON, Rand Corporation, Santa Monica, Calif.

GUY ORCUTT, Department of Economics, Harvard University, Cambridge, Mass.

HOWARD S. PIQUET, Legislative Reference Service, Library of Congress, Washington, D.C.

WILLIAM PRICE, Executive Director, Air Force Office of Scientific Research, Washington, D.C.

EVERETT M. ROGERS, Department of Communications, Michigan State University, East Lansing, Mich.

PAUL N. ROSENSTEIN-RODAN, Center for International Studies, Massachusetts Institute of Technology, Cambridge, Mass.

EDGAR SALIN, University of Basel, Basel, Switzerland

MARTIN SHUBIK, Department of Economics, Yale University, New Haven, Conn.

IRVIN H. SIEGEL, Senior Research Staff, The W. E. Upjohn Institute, Washington, D.C.

DANIEL L. SPENCER, Chairman, Department of Economics, Howard University, Washington, D.C.

INGVAR SVENNILSON, Socialvetens Kapliga Institute, Stockholm, Sweden

SIMON TEITEL, Center for Industrial Development, United Nations, New York, N.Y.

HENRY H. VILLARD, Chairman, Department of Economics, City College of New York, New York, N.Y.,

SAMUEL Z. WESTERFIELD, JR., Deputy Assistant Secretary for African Affairs, U. S. Department of State, Washington, D.C.

NATHANIEL WOLLMAN, Chairman, Department of Economics, University of New Mexico, Albuquerque, N.M.

ALEXANDER WORONIAK, Department of Economics, Catholic University of America, Washington, D.C.

PRAEGER SPECIAL STUDIES IN
INTERNATIONAL ECONOMICS AND DEVELOPMENT

Airlie House Conference on Transfer of Technology, 1966.

The Transfer of Technology to Developing Countries

Edited, with an Introduction and Summary, by
Daniel L. Spencer
and
Alexander Woroniak

FREDERICK A. PRAEGER, Publishers
New York · Washington · London

The purpose of the Praeger Special Studies is to make specialized research monographs in U.S. and international economics and politics available to the academic, business, and government communities. For further information, write to the Special Projects Division, Frederick A. Praeger, Publishers, 111 Fourth Avenue, New York, N.Y. 10003.

FREDERICK A. PRAEGER, PUBLISHERS
111 Fourth Avenue, New York, N.Y. 10003, U.S.A.
77-79 Charlotte Street, London W.1, England

Published in the United States of America in 1967
by Frederick A. Praeger, Inc., Publishers

Library of Congress Catalog Card Number: 67—25249

Printed in the United States of America

FOREWORD

"The United States and the West must either lead
in the process of modernizing the underdeveloped areas,
or by default contribute to a kind of world in which our
institutions and values cannot survive. " This statement
by Gabriel Almond echoes the thinking of a generation
of American leaders who have invested substantial
resources and other efforts in improving the conditions
of life in deficit areas in the hope that economic advance
would contribute to political stabilization and create the
soil in which democratic institutions might take root.

The easy optimism that flourished after World
War II has been jarred by the experience gained in two
decades of foreign aid and technical assistance to backward and stagnant areas. We have learned that neither
economic advance nor political stabilization can be
automatically initiated by the investment of U. S. resources. Dr. Carlos Chagas, President of the National
Academy of Sciences of Brazil, insists that the technological gap separating the advanced nations from the so-
called developing nations has grown wider rather than
narrower during the last decade, despite extensive
international cooperation. On a more hopeful note,
W. W. Rostow has postulated a theory of economic
evolution which includes a "take-off" stage where rapid
industrialization can be expected.

The chapters that follow were prepared by a group
of scholars who are too sophisticated to believe that rapid
economic development is a necessary consequence of
programs of material aid and technical assistance. While
they are fully capable as interpreters of economic history
and could develop attractive hypotheses relating to the
development of economic institutions, for the purposes
of this volume they have directed their attention to a
narrower field of economic theory in an attempt to
elucidate the processes of technological transfer and
structural change which are basic to economic advancement in backward areas.

Dr. Daniel L. Spencer was encouraged by the
Air Force Office of Scientific Research (AFOSR) to

conduct a conference on technological transfer, because it was felt that further useful work in this field might be stimulated by summing up the current state of knowledge and focusing attention on problems of a methodological and theoretical nature that are obstacles to further understanding of these important processes.

Our interest in problems of the kind submitted to the conference stems from the fact that the mission of AFOSR is to sponsor basic research in areas of potential applicability to the military. The present effort is part of a research program devoted to those scientific and technical fields which might serve to improve the manner in which U. S. military personnel, skills, equipment, and procurement policies can be exploited to the greatest benefit for the host country and to realize the U. S. national objectives of aiding our friends and strengthening our allies. There are many channels within the military services for the use of information derived from research on foreign economic development. Military assistance programs, mobile training teams, technical training, and advanced education provided by the U. S. services for foreign military personnel are some of the bridges to the field of application.

It is a source of gratification to the Air Force Office of Scientific Research that our expectations with regard to the conference on technological transfer and structural change have been fully realized. We think the results of the conference are an invaluable contribution to the study of the transfer of technology.

CHARLES E. HUTCHINSON
Air Force Office of Scientific Research

CONTENTS

LIST OF TABLES AND FIGURES

The Transfer of
Technology to
Developing Countries

INTRODUCTION

No phenomenon of the postwar world has caught the imagination of men more than the new technology and its potentialities. The advances in basic research and in industrial applications of research and development have been breathtaking, with benefits tangibly evident. Thinking men outside the dynamic countries which are the centers of innovation, research, and development become cognizant of the technological developments almost simultaneously with the innovating country's nationals. Correctly or incorrectly, leaders of emerging nations deem the technology essential as the prime propellant to growth and modernization, power and prestige, and they want to obtain this technology as quickly, cheaply, and efficiently as possible. Thus, the recent United Nations Conference on the Application of Science and Technology for the Benefit of Underdeveloped Areas produced hundreds of papers evidencing the interest in this subject from many points of view. How to transfer the technology emerges as a central theme.

It is in the stream of this world interest that the present volume is conceived. It is based on papers and proceedings of the Conference on Transfer of Technology at Airlie House, Warrenton, Virginia, in April, 1966. The Airlie House Conference grew out of research directed by Daniel L. Spencer and carried on, in association with Alexander Woroniak, in the Department of Economics at Howard University under the sponsorship of the U.S. Air Force Office of Scientific Research. The subject matter of the research was the economic implications of the transfer of technology, with special reference to the role of the military. The research has revealed that, among other channels, military organizations have played and can play an important role in transferring fundamental and advanced technology to foreign countries under appropriate conditions.

However, during the course of this work, it was found that various theoretical and operational aspects of the transfer of technology have been a relatively unstressed subject in economic literature. Whereas the other social sciences have paid more attention to the

1

matter of technological transfer, they have tended to submerge
the concept under generic and amorphous ideas such as diffusion and innovation, leaving the more teleological concept
of transfer undelineated. Economists, too, with some
notable exceptions, have been content to deal with technology
as if it had somehow arrived as a datum for incorporation
via market adjustments in general equilibrium theory, or a
"residual factor"--a shift in the production function. When
the specific idea of transfer of technology does appear, it
is often entwined with industrialization, social and revolutionary change, and other such sweeping ideas. It was the
feeling that the concept of technological transfer must be
treated as something specific, tangible, and utilitarian
that led to the convocation of a conference of prominent
economists. As anticipated, the papers, prepared comments,
and lively discussion summarized in this book provide evidence that the conference contributed to the understanding
of technological transfer, to its intellectual formulation,
to its testing as a concept, and to its utilization in various
ways, particularly for developing countries.

This book has been organized in eight chapters to
cover topics which seemed essential for examining the
concept of transfer of technology, its utility as a research
tool, and its operational potentiality. The rationale for
the selection of topics and their order of presentation lie
in an alternation between theory or policy and data or
operations in a spirit of scientific enquiry and exploration. The theme is the search for the optimum method
of transferring technology. The book follows the outline
on which the conference was based, except that the
general discussions are summarized and interpreted
in a single closing chapter. However, it should be borne
in mind that the topics of the discussions sometimes
depart significantly from the ground laid out in the
leading chapter. For example, the chapter by Professor
Kmenta was planned initially to set forth what economic
theory had to say about transfer of technology. Finding,
as he felt, that economic theory had little to offer,
Kmenta devised and presented ably his own theory,
centering on the technological gap. His ingenious
disclosure of a formalized technological lag theory is
a high point of economic analysis, but his premises

and methodology were brought under severe scrutiny as to
their adequacy. In the discussion, the ground often shifted
to delicate, institutional factors not covered in the model,
or intentionally omitted.

The chapters and discussion hold to the original
conference plan in most respects, with the result that there
is coherence in the end product. Lessons of economic
history are explored by Professor Murphy, who holds
that they are inapplicable to present-day complexities; Dr.
Salin summarizes the current position of modern Continental thought on transfer of technology, taking the framework
of Schumpeter as his point of departure. A theme of
diminishing availability of new technology in the developed
nations in conjunction with the Malthusian spectre in the
less-developed countries is presented by Dr. Hoselitz.
Lively opposition was stirred by Professor Chamberlain,
who lays out a carefully reasoned position on cultural and
institutional change via training and investment in human
capital. In a methodological chapter, Professor Shubik
examines the prospects for simulation in relation to transfer of technology and opens new horizons for future
exploration of transfer via simulation technique. Professor Svennilson provides a first formulation of strategy of
transfer, to which Professor Meier supplied an alternative modus operandi in the ensuing discussion. (See
Chapter 8.)

While the selection of topics was designed to bring
out what economics as a discipline might have to say
about transfer of technology to developing countries,
participants from other social sciences were invited to
provide soundings and confrontation. Indeed, confrontation was built into this study in other ways, as when,
for example, economists of an institutional or policy-
oriented disposition were brought to the table with
econometricians and other quantitatively oriented
scholars. Still further leavening was obtained by the
presence of administrators and physical scientists and
by a heavy admixture of foreign scholars.

The book represents a first attempt to examine
the transfer of technology to developing countries and

to assess the potentialities of the concept of technological transfer as a useful tool in modern economic analysis. While remaining exploratory in character, it delineates certain patterns of thought which may provide guidelines for policy-making and for further research. These thoughts are elaborated in the summary of the discussion provided in Chapter 8, but some highlights may be noted at this point. A predominant theme in all the chapters and discussions is the conflict between those scholars who view transfer as a simple imitative process, capable of inducing the appropriate cultural changes, and those who say, or come close to saying, that large revolutionary changes in non-Western societies are prerequisites for induction of modern technology. The fission between the imitationist school versus the cultural revolutionary doctrine is paralleled by, and related to, a dichotomy over the choice of technology to be transferred. The imitationists generally opt for the latest technology; the cultural revolutionists look to older technology, or to technology specially adjusted to local factor proportions with the assistance of indigenous innovators or entrepreneurs.

There are, of course, lacunae that hindsight can discern. The study perhaps overemphasizes the problems of the donee country. With some exceptions, little attention is paid to the problems of the donor countries. Questions of donor-country adjustment to new export patterns introduced by borrowed technology in developing countries were raised but not pursued. Similarly, appropriate donor-country policy regarding technology was mentioned but given little attention. These and other matters will perhaps be given further research.

The actual accomplishments of this conference are, indeed, significant. First, the book confirms what prior research had already concluded: that the study of the transfer of technology has been a neglected area in social science, especially in economics. Second, the concept of technological transfer has been clarified and generally established as a useful tool for economic theory and operational application by a representative group of economists, social scientists, and others. Third, important methodological issues were spotlighted in the criticism of the relevance of the linear homogeneous production function. Fourth, the possibilities of simulation and related techniques were laid open for further analysis and use. Fifth, an attempt has been made to supply a nexus between technological transfer and American and Continental thought, as well as to examine the relationship between transfer of technology and prior historical experience. Sixth, the modern issues of hard-nosed versus soft-nosed approaches to transferring technology was explored. The imitationist school confronted a school of cultural revolutionists, who feel that the shock of social change consequent to the introduction of technology must be socially engineered. Seventh, a beginning strategy for technological transfer appeared, perhaps as a result of a marriage between the opposing schools. Svennilson, Meier, and others have provided some formal insights along these lines, and from their thoughts on strategy, one is left with the impression that embryonic technology requies very powerful promotional institutions--instituciones di fomento, the military, or the big international company--if it is to be effectively transferred.

These remarks scarcely do justice to the wealth of ideas brought out in this volume. Perusal of the book undoubtedly will yield many suggestive lines of thought. In this, it is believed, will be found the ultimate value of the invenstment made by our sponsors and of the efforts of the contributing scholars.

DANIEL L. SPENCER

ALEXANDER WORONIAK

1

RETROSPECT AND PROSPECT

by John Joseph Murphy

The problem of how to increase the rate of economic growth of less-developed economies has led to increased interest on the part of economists in the diffusion of technology from one nation to another. One phase of this interest has involved a reexamination of the historical experiences of developed nations in an effort to determine what factors aided and/or hindered technological transfer and diffusion in earlier time periods.[1] Following this line of inquiry, the specific objective of this chapter is to draw upon the nineteenth-century experiences of the nations of Western Europe and the United States in order to show the relevance of past movements to the current efforts to transfer technology from advanced to developing nations.

Before reaching its concluding section, the chapter will deal with the nature of technology; with an examination of how selected technological advances were transferred among the nations of Western Europe and the United States; and with an analysis of the way in which economic growth, the availability of resources and labor supplies, and the actions of governments aided or hindered this process.

THE CONCEPT OF TECHNOLOGY

Technology, and consequently technological diffusion, have been conceptualized in a number of ways, each of which suggests different theoretical and historical approaches. The simplest version views technology as involving only changes in artifacts. A more sophisticated approach adds to the physical objects, labor and managerial skills. This approach is susceptible to aggregate analysis, and economic theorists and historians have made wide use of it. A third approach views technology as a "socio-technological" phenomena; that is, besides involving material and artifact improvements, technology is considered to incorporate a cultural, social, and psychological process as well.[2] In this view any detail of change, if it is to be effective and if the ultimate repercussions are to be anticipated, must be related to

the "central values of the culture. "[3] Although some
economists, such as Professor Hagen, have made such
a cultural approach central to their theory of development, [4] most economists reject it on the assumption
that for their tasks cultural variables can normally be
taken as constant. Thus, economists do not reject the
importance of noneconomic variables, only the necessity of concentrating upon them.

While each of the above approaches can be
useful for a given line of investigation, for the usual
purposes of the economic historian they are either
too narrow or too broad. A much more meaningful
approach is one that falls between reliance upon technology as total cultural change, and reliance upon
technology as just the direct relation between capital
and cooperating labor. The economic historian has
to recognize that machines operate with more than
complementary factors of production; they also require complementary economic units. The success
of any technological change, therefore, is contingent
upon the ability of other operations to adapt their
mode of action to the necessities of the innovation.
From the wheel to the computer, success has been
dependent upon the invention being integrated into a
process, and often upon creating a process that
demanded a new system of production. Technology,
therefore, is embodied not in aggregate capital, nor
in particular factors, but in the whole economic
process that extends from factor supplies on the one
hand to the marketing outlets on the other. It implies
an interrelatedness not only within a firm but between
firms, and even between industries. It involves the
harmonious meshing of a number of subsystems.
This makes technological transfer and diffusion a
function of the ability to change processes that require
system adaptations.

Inasmuch as it is in the nature of a system
both to tend toward self-maintenance and to place
limitations upon the compatibility of certain parts,
for technological change to be introduced successfully, the component parts of the existing system

must be able to adapt to it. This does not mean that just
one set of systems is capable of providing the correct
adaptation. It does mean that the technological process
 places limits within which the system has to adapt, and
that these limits involve such factors as internal machine-
labor ratios (including the quality of labor that operates
with the machines), internal organization of the enterprise, the end of the enterprise, and external structures.

This approach to technology assumes that any
given technical change is "interrelated," to use Frankel's
term, to other input-output factors regardless of whether
these factors are internal or external to the firm or
industry. [5] It does not assume, however, that "interrelatedness means that single components of a productive process cannot be replaced on a 'one-at-a-time'
basis."[6] Such an assumption constricts the concept
into an untenable straight-jacket wherein the whole of
any process would have to be changed in order to introduce a sectoral innovation. What is being argued here
is that the technical components of one process may
not be transferred to another process without transferring or developing compatible system components.
Within any given process, however, advances can be
made within sectors--that is, on a "one-at-a-time"
basis--and it is precisely such advantages that may
create tensions that call forth advances in other
sectors. Where this does occur, a cumulative movement evolves into a new process wherein it might not
be possible to transfer any single component back
into the original process.

Because technology is a process, the ability
to diffuse technology is determined by the amount and
type of system changes that are a necessary concomitant to the incorporation of any technical change
into an equilibrium situation. These system changes
to be effectuated will require both economic and value
modifications, and these modifications will have to
occur before diffusion can proceed to the point where
the technology can be considered as the norm of the
economy.

Because technology is a process, any given technical change starts a sequence of actions that create areas wherein adjustments (innovations?) have to be made in order to reestablish an equilibrium situation. These adjustments may provide "a setting of the stage" that can lead to acts of insight that start another sequence of actions. [7] And in certain cases--not necessarily involving major innovations--technical changes may establish technological processes that contain in themselves conditions that favor a continuous evolution of the technological processes.

TRANSFERS IN THE NINETEENTH CENTURY

Both the transfer of technology across national borders and the diffusion of technology within nation-states were much faster in the nineteenth century than in any previous period in human history. This speed, how-ever, was relative to a select geographic area and to a very small number of technical changes. And by modern expectations, it was much too slow.

For diffusion within a nation-state, the best generalization is that it took more than two generations from the appearance of major technical innovations until they had become characteristic features of the most advanced economy. Watt's steam engine of 1776, for example, did not begin "to play an important part in powering the British economy" until the 1830's or 1840's, and steam power was not introduced on a mas-sive scale until the last three decades of the century. [8]

Watt's engine was introduced into France in 1779 by the Periers, but forty years later only 200 steam engines were being used to power French industry. [9] By the mid-nineteenth century, French statistics indicate 6,800 steam engines were in use, but these, even for that time, were relatively low-powered and were certainly far from sufficient for steam to be described as a major source of power for French industry.

Prior to Watt's invention, steam engines were used in Germany for pumping out mines, but these engines had the same deficiencies that Watt was attempting to overcome. [10]   Reden introduced a Watt engine into Germany in 1788 but the pace of internal diffusion that followed was slower even than in France.   In fact, so slowly did things move "that in 1837... all the territories of Prussia, including the coal fields on both sides of the Rhine, that of the Saar, and that of Upper Silesia, were only employing 7500 h. p. for mining, metallurgy, spinning, milling and every other purpose.... "[11]

South of the Alps, diffusion of the steam engine proceeded at an even slower pace.   Count Porro Lambertenghi introduced steam power into the emerging textile industry of Italy in 1816.   But such nonhuman power had not been diffused sufficiently prior to the outbreak of World War I to permit power-driven machines to be a characteristic feature in the Italian woolen industry. [12]

The diffusion of steam engines also took considerable time on the western side of the Atlantic.   Introduced into the United States before the end of the eighteenth century, steam engines, although they found ready acceptance as power sources for river boats, were not generally introduced into American industry until after the Civil War.

As the dates associated with the first introduction into each nation show, the transfer of the steam engine across national borders was much faster than its diffusion within national boundaries.   A similar experience is found in the basic equipment that resulted in the industrialization of cotton textiles.   Within about five years after Hargreaves developed a workable jenny, the instrument was introduced into France, but it "did not come quickly into very general use. "[13]   Arkwright's water frame followed a similar path, reaching France in the 1780's and Germany in the 1790's, only to stagnate for decades before being generally accepted. [14]   The mule and the power loom did not fare much better.   Clapham reports that it was not until 1871 that the power loom "was well on the road to victory" over the hand industry in Germany, the same time that machine spinning came to replace hand spinning in that country. [15]

Progress was somewhat faster in France, especially in the east in the Alsace region. Here the power loom may have been adopted more quickly than it was in Lancashire.[16] The self-actor mule, however, was not readily accepted, and in fact, did not become characteristic in France until the 1860's.[17] In the northern and southern regions of France diffusion was much slower than in Alsace, being as much as a generation behind in the textile firms located in the south.[18]

Italy once again lagged behind the countries north of the Alps as the Italian cotton textile industry developed very slowly from the introduction of the first mechanical spinning jenny in 1808. As Professor Clough notes, it was only after the unification of the 1860's that "the mechanization of the textile trades went on at a more rapid pace."[19]

The initial innovations in textile machinery did not move westward from England as fast as they moved across the channel, but once they did cross the Atlantic they found much more fruitful soil. From Slatter's introduction of Arkwright's frames in the 1790's and Lowell's variation on power looms introduced in the middle 1810's, diffusion within the United States proceeded at a much faster pace than within the Continental industries. Not only was transfer and diffusion occurring, but the Americans were very quickly beginning to introduce their own variations. By the end of the 1830's some observers were suggesting that in some areas, such as power for weaving, the Americans had already surpassed the British.[20]

The American woolen industry was making similar advances. In the early decades of the century the American industry copied the technology developed in the English industry, but by the 1830's indigenous technological developments began to occur, and it then became England's turn to have to adopt advances made abroad.[21]

Some significant technological developments of the
nineteenth century were transferred at a slower rate than
those so far noted, and even larger gaps came to appear
between nations. This was especially true in the technical developments that occurred in the making of tools
and in the peculiar arrangements which came to be called
the American system. It was also true in the numerous
minor modifications made of major innovations.

Between 1775 and 1850, in response to the needs of
expanding industries, improvements in machines to make
machines came in rapid succession from a variety of
English and American inventors. These tools, ranging
from engine lathes and planers to turret lathes and milling machines, are claimed by some to be the primary
focus for industrialization. [22] They not only increased
the speed and the efficiency with which power could be
utilized, but they decreased the amount of skill required
by machine operators. More important, the production
of these machines in a distinct tool industry came to
provide "a center for the acquisition and diffusion of
new skills and techniques in a machinofacture type of
economy. "[23]

Such tools initially came into existence from the
operations of tool divisions of other enterprises, but by
mid-century specialized machine tool producers had
emerged in England and the United States. While the
English producers were more numerous and capable
of producing machines at lower prices, they were
beginning to be surpassed in the production of specialized function machines by the American shops. [24]
Within the next generation the American machine tool
industry continued to concentrate on the production of
specialized equipment, but in the process it proceeded
to lower its cost of production well under its English
competitors. [25]

On the Continent the situation was quite
different. A British Parliamentary Committee noted
in 1841 that machine shops across the channel were
capable of turning out special-purpose machine tools,
but that this was primarily done for internal firm
consumption. [26] This left most manufacturers in the

position of having to purchase their capital equipment
from British producers, and for many industrial
operations this situation did not change over the next
seventy years.

The most striking example is Italy. The
Italians did not even benefit from the backward linkage between textiles and tools, which characterized
most other textile industries, as is seen by the fact
that at the outbreak of World War I, nearly 90 per
cent of the equipment in use in the Italian textile
industry had been made in England. Although numerous
explanations can be given for the slow rate of development of a machine tool industry in Italy, it is widely
accepted that the absence of this industry was itself a
causative factor in the generally slow rate of economic
growth of the nation. [27]

France, although not as weak in machine tool
production as Italy, was significantly behind England
and the United States by the end of the century. Small
shops directed by exceptionally conservative entrepreneurs[28] dominated the industry and left the French
in the unenviable position when war came of having to
make "great efforts... to develop the output of machine
tools. "[29]

Of all the Continental countries, Germany adopted
the most readily the advances made in tool manufacturing. The ability to produce machines, which removed
the work from human hands, made the Germans the leading Continental exporter of machine tools as the twentieth
century began. In the rapid development of the German
economy after 1870, German industry also began to make
significant use of a system of standardized and interchangeable parts production. In this regard, Germany
quickly became superior to Britain, the only other major
European nation to have introduced the new "methods"
of production. But as Landes observes, the ultimate
form of this system, mass production, did not come in
either European nation until the "rationalization" of the
1920's. [30]

This was a considerable lag behind the United States in which the system of standardized parts had progressed by the middle of the nineteenth century to the point that it was viewed as a characteristic feature of most advanced American industries. [31] Introduced into the making of guns at the start of the century, the process of interchangeable parts production was initially diffused very slowly. [32] After the depression of 1837, however, it came to be incorporated in almost every sector of American industrial activity. As the century progressed, the idea of interchangeable parts, standardized production, and quantity output continuously evolved until it found its ultimate principle in Henry Ford's assembly line of 1913.

Of the technological changes discussed in this chapter, it was in the use of the American system that the British fell behind very early. The concept was carried eastward across the Atlantic into the government arms factory at Enfield in the 1850's--on the advice of a government investigation team--but British producers failed to accept the system. In one of the ironies of economic history, it was even rejected by the skilled artisans of the British horological trades, the direct descendants of the men who were responsible for providing the base for the British industrial revolution. [33] When they were faced in the mid-nineteenth century with the competition of the low-priced products, which the American system enabled American watch and clock factories to market, the British horological trade, horrified at the prospects of substituting machines for their skilled hands, vehemently rejected the whole notion. [34] This type of economic irrationality on the part of British industries as the century progressed has often been noted, but it should be emphasized that such decisions were made in processes dominated by very skilled craftsmen and not in areas dominated by illiterate and superstitious peasants.

This, of course, has not been an attempt to provide an exhaustive survey of the international transfer and domestic diffusion of technology in the nineteenth century. It has attempted to highlight the fact that with some of the most important technological developments, the Western European and North American nations started at about the same time. Over the course of the century, however, they came to diffuse these changes at different paces and then came to develop new forms of technology which were not as rapidly transferred across national borders. These observations automatically lead to the question: Why? Why are some innovations transferred faster than others? Why are they diffused at different paces after being transferred? And, maybe most important of all, why is one nation a leader in one area only to be a laggard in another?

TRANSFER, DIFFUSION, AND TECHNOLOGICAL PROCESS

Explanations ranging from relative factor endowments to social rigidities have been given in answer to such questions, but the importance attached to specific causative factors tends to shift from one case study to another. The manner in which each of these factors affects the rate of transfer and diffusion, however, is more constant. To transfer or diffuse technology successfully, all of the components of the existing process must be able to adjust to the requirements of the innovated feature. Such adjustments can or will occur only if all participating systems are able, or willing, or forced to acclimate themselves to the demands of the new process. Thus, the obstacles to transfer or diffusion, whether they be relative factor supplies or social rigidities, manifest themselves within the specifications of process adjustment and system adaptation that a new technical change requires.

Within this framework many factors can legitimately be considered as relevant to technological innovation and diffusion, but this chapter will consider only the following four: the general rate of economic growth, resource availability, labor availability, and government action. To argue that growth is necessary in order to bring about technological change and that technological change is necessary in order to bring about growth is to get involved in one of the chicken

and egg situations open to the economic historian. Yet
the issue cannot be sidestepped in any attempt to analyze
technological innovation and diffusion.

The importance of economic growth in stimulating
process changes is clearly seen in the early major
innovations introduced in the British textile industry.[35]
Expanding demand for cloth created bottlenecks in the
existing process which stimulated new ways of production. For a time, each introduced technical change
developed a process that involved new gaps and was,
therefore, somewhat unstable. With a continuous expansion in demand being exerted against these somewhat
unstable processes, the British entrepreneurs were under
pressure to develop new technical adjustments which, in
turn, led to new processes.

Most of these technical developments did not
require major adjustments of the existing process, but
the sum total of the adjustments did result in revolutionary
process changes. Not only was the factory system a
necessary concomitant of all of these technical developments, but the large-scale production that they made
possible, required advances in raw material production
techniques, and "the support of an organized system of
transport, commerce, and credit."[36]

The fact that the technological innovations in
cotton textiles required other innovations in the over-all
process of production does not explain why these improvements first took place in England, nor why they were
diffused so slowly in other countries. One possible
answer to the former question is that England possessed
in the artisans of its engineering trades concentrated
quantities of a necessary factor supply for developing
and producing the requisite machines and tools. The
British, therefore, could make use of an existing
process of production to meet one of the prime requirements of the new process of textile production.

Britain was not the only nation whose handicraft
textile industry was under pressure from demand, or
out of balance between spinners' output and weavers'
need, or in possession of skilled tool makers. Although

Britain may have been so much more favorably situated
that she was able to take the lead, other nations were
certainly situated favorably enough to have adopted
British technical developments at a more rapid rate.
To explain why they did not, it is necessary to consider
two other process factors.

One is the difference in the marketing processes
available on the two sides of the channel. Habakkuk
assigns to this factor the predominant role in his
explanation of the slow rate of diffusion of textile technology on the continent. [37] But, in accepting the differences in marketing procedures, Habakkuk is expressing
only a relative importance over other process factors,
including the type of available labor. Labor considerations seem to me, however, to be more crucial for
obtaining process changes.

It was this factor which gave to England an over-
whelming advantage. Compared to the labor supply on
the Continent, British labor was more mobile and more
willing to work within a factory on a full-time basis,
and British entrepreneurs were more willing to hire
them under such conditions. [38] Thus, in addition to
pressures from an expanding market demand, the
British textile industry was capable of moving faster
and further in process changes because of the existence
of a necessary technical linkage, a necessary market
structure, and a more adaptable labor supply.

In the early stage of industrial development,
Britain also gained process advantages because of her
natural resource endowment. Edward Baines noted
this advantage in 1835 when he suggested that England
had no fear from the French textile industry because
"France has natural disadvantages, especially in the
comparative scarcity of fuel and iron. "[39] Clapham
also found the French natural resource disadvantage
to be a reason "much more permanent and deep-
seated than revolution and war to explain why no
amount of intelligent official action could make France
follow in England's steps at England's pace. "[40]

Scarcity of natural resources is an impediment to technological diffusion, however, only if an absolutely necessary process requires a specific raw material which cannot be imported at a cost that would be low enough to make the end result of the process competitive, at least in the home market. This is a rigid condition, which became less applicable as developments within the nineteenth century began to make alternative processes possible, or to make imported items effective substitutes for inefficient domestic supplies. The former condition is illustrated by the development of the Gilchrist-Thomas procedure for converting high phosphoric iron ores into steel. The latter condition has recently been cited by Kindleberger to argue that the French lack of coal was no handicap to general French development from at least 1830 on. [41]

Of the possible explanations for the establishment, retardation, or redirection of technological diffusion, the factor proportions relation is the most appealing to economists. In its simplest form, this explanation finds the rate of technological change determined by the size of the labor force relative to other factor supplies, particularly capital. Thus, Clough notes that in Italy labor was so cheap "that there was less of an incentive to replace men with machines than in those economies where labor was scarce."[42] Habakkuk argues the reverse for the United States. [43]

Unfortunately, the issue is not as simple as these two judgments might suggest, for in the nineteenth century, technological transfer and diffusion depended as much upon the relative qualities of the labor force as upon its relative quantities. The superior skill of English workmen, for example, provided England with a considerable technological advantage in the early nineteenth century. [44] This advantage remained, however, only as long as technical changes did not impinge upon the traditional process of artisan production. When the artisan system itself was required to change, it became difficult, and at times impossible, for British craftsmen to introduce technological innovations or to adopt innovations made elsewhere. Thus, the British watch- and clockmakers

made choices leading to destruction while maintaining
their artisan traits, rather than to survive by introducing the more efficient machine process developed in the
United States. In this matter they showed the characteristic of British engineers who were, as S. B. Saul has
noted, "obsessed by the technical product rather than by
the technique of production."[45]

Experiences of labor forces on the Continent
also show the importance of the quality of the skilled
labor force. Great attention has been paid to the development in Germany of technical education and to the contribution that it made to German industrial advancement at
the end of the century. Not enough attention has been
paid to the fact that this emphasis coincided with the
development of industrial processes--primarily in
chemicals and steel--which would make better use of
the engineer and scientist than of the craftsman and tool
maker. By accident or design, Germany developed an
educational framework that meshed with the process
requirements of the current industrial frontier.

In addition to some quantities of skilled labor
needed to develop and/or accept technological process
changes, some minimum level of training for the mass
of laborers is of crucial importance. The inability of
illiterate or totally untrained labor to handle machines
necessary for even simple industrialization processes
extends from the earliest introduction of textile manufacturing in England[46] to its diffusion on the Continent.[47]
This point is illustrated by an almost infinite number of
examples given in the recent literature on economic
development. With untrained labor supplies, rational
short-run economic decisions lead to the utilization of
capital of limited technological sophistication. This
may result in the development of processes that hinder
the later acceptance or diffusion of technological
advances associated with more advanced stages of
industrial development.

Skilled and flexible labor, however, can operate
within processes which create both the demand for new
technology and the supply of the same. This is seen, in

a striking way, in the development of the machine tool
industries and in the development of the system of
interchangeable parts production. Both of these activities
require significant supplies of skilled, specialized labor,
whose own process of production depends to a considerable extent upon changes occurring in other processes.
Thus, in contrast to a country like Italy where a machine
tool industry was late in developing, the United States
gained from the convergence of knowledge, supply, and
demand that accompanied the development of the American
machine tool industry. In contrast to England, where
machine tool production did develop but under a craft
tradition, the United States gained by the willingness of
American labor to incorporate machines in new ways. [48]
The result was a technological process, whose transfer
to and diffusion in other nations demanded more than the
acceptance of particular machines or even a particular
sequence of machines.

Such industries also aid technological change
because of the particular expertise they supply to other
industries. In Usher's terms, they provide the particular sequence of events that permits those insights
which result in industrial innovation. And it seems
reasonable to argue that if technical change is more
important than capital formation in bringing about
economic growth, then such industries contribute far
more to growth than other industries, such as possibly
textiles.

In the international transmission of technology,
nineteenth-century governments did not play the positive
role followed by governments in modern developing
economies. The governments of England and the United
States, for the most part, reacted in a neutral manner
to technological transfer. Some European governments,
however, did provide limited assistance by supplying
effective patent protection, financial assistance, or
specialized educational institutions. Some of the
policies of Continental governments, however, impeded
technological transfer. This was particularly true of
certain tariffs put into effect in France and Italy, and
these policies may have had greater impact than those
that were intended to assist technological transfer.

As governments in the nineteenth century--with
the possible exception of the Japanese--played only
marginal roles in the transfer and diffusion of technology,
no firm judgment concerning the correct function of
government can be reached.   One can only presume that,
in some instances, the results desired might have been
more quickly achieved   had the government acted positively.   But as with all presumptions, there is no firm
basis for accepting this one over its opposite; i.e.,
transfer and diffusion on the whole might have been
slower than they were if governments had played a more
active role.

PROSPECTS IN RETROSPECT

The ease with which key innovations, such as
the frame or the steam engine, were transferred across
national borders indicates that initially they were not
confined to a process which is complicatedly interrelated or unique to a given nation.   The differences
in the ability to diffuse these innovations within each
country, however, show that enough differences in
systems and processes existed to require different
adjustments.   As diffusion did occur, new processes
that involved more complex interrelationships (and in
some instances unique characteristics) began to emerge.
These developments resulted in such vast changes that,
by the end of the century, the possibility of transferring
and diffusing the most advanced technology was confined
to a small group of countries that had already made
appropriate process and system changes.   For those
countries that ended the nineteenth century much as
they began it, the possibilities of absorbing advanced
technology became more limited because of the vast
number of system changes that had first to occur.

Veblen and Gerschenkron, each in his own time
and in his own way, have suggested that, instead of
a disadvantage, it may be an advantage to be "backward"
in the technological race.[49]   But, if there are advantages,
they accrue to those who are not too backward.   Professor
Singer has rightly argued that a latecomer is now faced

with a serious disadvantage because the capital-intensive
technology of the more advanced economies involves a
heavy initial investment, is too complicated to be produced domestically, requires the saving of labor, and
suffers from a high rate of obsolescence. [50] To this, I
would add that it also requires a process package,
which is beyond the capacity of many countries to assimi-
late, given the structure of their existing processes and
systems.

The historical record of technological diffusion,
when viewed as a diffusion of a process, indicates three
potential points of interest for the "prospects" of the less-
developed countries. First, it suggests that Staley and
Morse's emphasis upon the role of small industries is
exceptionally important. Not only do small industries
demand less internal process arrangements, but by
their specialized nature, they also demand fewer external
contacts. What Staley and Morse note about the modern
artisan is also true for most small-scale industries:
"The hallmark of the artisan in the modern economy is
not lack of machines or of up-to-date techniques, but
individualized production or service. "[51]

Second, the experience of the United States in
particular suggests that highly specialized training,
whether of the engineering category or the vocational
category, may tend to create in a dynamic system as
many obstacles to diffusion as it overcomes. Any
student of comparative economic development in the
nineteenth century must be impressed by the ability
of the American worker to adapt to new ways, and to
the fact that this was aided by his lack of training in
a given line of endeavor. In a dynamic world where
artifact changes require process changes and system
interactions, the ability of the worker to reason appears
much more important than his ability to perform a
specific function.

Third, as limited as the nineteenth-century
experience is, it does suggest that the government can
play a positive role in technological diffusion. But, to
do so the government has to attempt to structure the

whole of a technological process and not just a component
of it.   This may require concentration upon a single line
of development in order to prevent uncoordinated inter-
vention that may do more harm than good.   At the same
time it must be recognized that governments can also
hinder diffusion, as they did in the nineteenth century.
Thus, government stimulation instead of government
determination may provide less chance for errors that
could cause major lags.

The differences between the world of today and
the world wherein modern industrialization began are so
significant that the possibility of drawing any real
prospects out of retrospect are slim.   One can observe
that knowledge of the existence of technical components
has increased with improved communications and improved
levels of literacy, and that this should tend to increase the
transfer of technology.   One can also observe that the
quantity and quality of complementary factor supplies is
a prime consideration for efficiently utilizing a given
technological process, and therefore, that the closer a
foreign technology is related to the type of factor supplies
available domestically, the easier transfer and diffusion
should become.

Unfortunately, the technological processes of the
developed countries, and the factor supplies and the
operational processes of the developing countries have
moved in opposite directions over the last century and a
half.   These movements have more than offset the
increased ease of acquiring knowledge with the result
that the transfer of technology from the leaders to the
followers may now be more difficult.

NOTES

1. Although the footnotes will provide numerous references to relevant historical works, particular note must be made of Professor Landes' extensive survey and of Professor Habakkuk's pioneering attempt at comparative analysis of technological progress. David S. Landes, "Technological Change and Development in Western Europe, 1750-1914," in H. J. Habakkuk and M. Postan (eds.), The Cambridge Economic History of Europe, Vol. VI, No. I (Cambridge, Eng.: University Press, 1965); and H. J. Habakkuk, American and British Technology in the Nineteenth Century (Cambridge, Eng.: University Press, 1962).

2. George M. Foster, Traditional Cultures, and the Impact of Technological Change (New York: Harper & Row, 1962), p. 2.

3. Margaret Mead (ed.), Cultural Patterns and Technical Change (New York: Columbia University Press, 1955), pp. 12-13.

4. Everett E. Hagen, On the Theory of Social Change (Homewood, Ill.: Dorsey Press, 1962).

5. Marvin Frankel, "Obsolescence and Technological Change in a Maturing Economy," American Economic Review, XLV (June, 1955), 296-319.

6. Edward Ames and Nathan Rosenberg, "Changing Technological Leadership and Industrial Growth," Economic Journal, LXXIII (March, 1963), 23.

7. Abbott Payson Usher, A History of Mechanical Inventions (Rev. ed.; Cambridge, Mass: Harvard University Press, 1954), pp. 65-67.

8. H. J. Habakkuk and Phyllis Deane, "The Take-off in Britain," in W. W. Rostow (ed.), The Economics of Take-off into Sustained Growth (New York: St. Martin's Press, 1963), p. 72.

9.   Rondo E. Cameron, France and the Economic Development of Europe 1800-1914: Conquests of peace and seeds of war (Princeton, N. J. : Princeton University Press, 1961), 7; W. O. Henderson, Britain and Industrial Europe, 1750-1870 (Liverpool: University Press of Liverpool, 1954), p. 46.

10.   Fritz Redlich, "The Leaders of the German Steam-Engine Industry During the First Hundred Years," Journal of Economic History, IV (November, 1944), 121-48.

11.   J. H. Clapham, The Economic Development of France and Germany 1815-1914 (3rd ed. ; Cambridge, Eng: Cambridge University Press, 1928), p. 89.

12.   Shepard B. Clough, The Economic History of Modern Italy (New York: Columbia University Press, 1964), pp. 61-64.

13.   Henderson, op. cit. , p. 21.

14.   Landes, op. cit. , pp. 368-69.

15.   Clapham, op. cit. , p. 297; W. G. Hoffman, "The Take-off in Germany," in Rostow (ed.), The Economics of Take-off into Sustained Growth, p. 109.

16.   Clapham, op. cit. , pp. 65-66.

17.   Clapham, op. cit. , p. 242; Landes, op. cit., p. 389.

18.   Landes, op. cit. , p. 391.

19.   Clough, op. cit. , p. 61.

20.   James Montgomery, A Practical Detail of the Cotton Manufacture of the United States of America (Glasgow, 1840), p. 82.

21.   Arthur H. Cole, The American Woolen Manufacture (Cambridge, Mass. : Harvard University Press, 1926), I, 120 ff. Cole claims England did not regain the lead until the 1860's. (P. 127)

22. Abbott Payson Usher, "The Industrialization of Modern Britain," Technology and Culture, I (Spring, 1960), 113.

23. Nathan Rosenberg, "Technological Change in the Machine Tool Industry, 1840-1910," Journal of Economic History, XXIII (December, 1963), p. 425.

24. Great Britain, Parliamentary Papers, Vol. I (Accounts and Papers, Vol. II), 1854-55, "Report of the Committee on the Machinery of the United States of America," pp. 539-633. Substantial excerpts from this report are given in John E. Sawyer, "The Social Basis of the American System of Manufacturing," Journal of Economic History, XIV (December, 1954), 361-79.

25. W. Paul Strassmann, Risk and Technological Innovation: American Manufacturing Methods During the Nineteenth Century (Ithaca: Cornell University Press, 1959), p. 117. Also see "Power and Machinery Employed in Manufactures," U. S., Bureau of the Census, Tenth Census of the United States: 1880. Manufacturing, XXII.

26. Great Britain, Parliamentary Papers (Accounts and Papers, Vol. VII), 1841, "Report from the Select Committee Appointed to Inquire into the Operation of the Existing Laws Affecting the Exportation of Machinery."

27. Clough, op. cit., p. 82; Alexander Gerschenkron, "Notes on the Rate of Industrial Growth in Italy, 1881-1913," Journal of Economic History, XV (December, 1955), 368-70, reprinted in Alexander Gerschenkron, Economic Backwardness in Historical Perspective (Cambridge, Mass.: Harvard University Press, 1962), pp. 82-83.

28. Clapham, op. cit., p. 242. Clapham states that the average shop "in 1913 employed only 150-175 men." Also see the notations "on the inertia and excessive prudence of the mechanical industry" from a report of the Ministère du Commerce given in Charles P. Kindleberger, Economic Growth in France and Britain 1851-1950 (Cambridge, Mass.: Harvard University Press, 1964), pp. 119-20.

29.   Arthur Fontaine, French Industry During the War (New Haven: Yale University Press, 1927), p. 95.

30.   Landes, op. cit. , pp. 543-44;   also see Robert A. Brady, The Rationalization Movement in German Industry: A study in the evolution of economic planning (Berkeley: University of California Press, 1933), chaps. ii and vii.

31.   See sources cited in footnote 24.

32.   George Taylor claims "that the technical superiority of the new method was not generally recognized for small arms until about 1827. " The Transportation Revolution (New York: Rinehart, 1951), pp. 221-22   Shortly after Whitney introduced the system in arms manufacturing it was introduced independently in the making of clocks.   Here the impact was faster; the new system being characteristic by the early 1820's.   See my "Entrepreneurship in the Establishment of the American Clock Industry, " Journal of Economic History, XXVI (June, 1966), 169-86.

33.   W. Bowden, M. Karpovich, and A. P. Usher, An Economic History of Europe Since 1750 (New York: American Book Co. , 1938), p. 307.   A British clock- and watchmaker testified before a Parliamentary Committee that the machinery of the cotton and woolen factories "were invented by, and yet are mostly constructed, repaired, and superintended by artists of the clock and watchmaking trade. " "Report from the Select Committee on the Petitions of the Watchmakers of Coventry, &c. , " Great Britain, Parliamentary Papers (Sessional Papers, Vol. VI), 1817, pp. 43-44.

34.   See the extensive debates on this topic that were printed in the Horological Journal between 1860 and 1867.

35. Pre-growth is neither a sufficient nor a necessary condition for technological change. This is seen in the numerous industries that have undertaken large expansion programs without introducing new technology, and in the many innovations introduced for which demand then had to be created.

36. T. S. Ashton, The Industrial Revolution 1760-1830 (London: Oxford University Press, 1948), p. 44.

37. H. J. Habakkuk, "The Historical Experience on the Basic Conditions of Economic Progress," in Leon H. Dupriez (ed.), Economic Progress (Louvain, Belgium: Institut de Recherches Economiques et Sociales, 1955), p. 160.

38. In 1835, Edward Baines wrote that the French "weavers, and even many of the spinners, cannot be induced to work the year round at their looms or mules, but in the months of summer and vintage turn to agricultural pursuits for relaxation; a practice which. . . most seriously interrupts the operations of the manufactory." History of the Cotton Manufacture in Great Britain (London: H. M. Fisher, 1835), pp. 512-13. Also see A. W. Coats, "Changing Attitudes to Labour in the Mid-Eighteenth Century," Economic History Review, 2nd-ser. XI (August, 1958), 35-51.

39. Baines, op. cit., p. 513.

40. Clapham, op. cit., p. 56.

41. Kindleberger, op. cit., pp. 17-29.

42. Clough, op. cit., p. 58.

43. H. J. Habakkuk, American and British Technology in the Nineteenth Century, passim.

44. cf. Mary Jean Bowman, "From Guilds to Infant Training Industries, " in C. Arnold Anderson and Mary Jean Bowman (eds.), Education and Economic Development (Chicago: Aldine Publishing Co. , 1965), p. 105.

45. S. B. Saul, "The Motor Industry in Britain to 1914, " Business History, V (December, 1962), 22-44.

46. See, for example, the comments given in Andrew Ure, Philosophy of Manufactures (London: C. Knight, 1835).

47. In testimony before a Parliamentary Committee in 1841, J. E. Tennant stated: "the use of the power loom is so imperfect in their (Saxon) hands that it becomes a much dearer instrument of production than the handloom itself. " Quoted in W. O. Henderson, op. cit. , p. 143.

48. The Welsh emigrant who "would have recognized the machinery of an American (tin) mill in 1890" but "would have been a stranger to its arrangement and operation" was not an isolated phenomenon. C. W. Pursell, "Tariff and Technology: The Foundation and Development of the American Tinplate Industry, 1872-1900, " Technology and Culture, III (Summer, 1962) 280.

49. Thorstein Veblen, Imperial Germany and the Industrial Revolution (New York: Sentry Press, 1964); Alexander Gerschenkron, Economic Backwardness in Historical Perspective, esp. chap. 1. Neither advocates that backwardness must convey an advantage, only that it may, if other factors are right. See particularly Gerschenkron, pp. 44, 51.

50. Hans W. Singer, "Obstacles to Economic Development, " Social Research, XX (Spring, 1953), 20; reprinted in H. W. Singer International Development: Growth and Change (New York: McGraw-Hill, 1964), p. 60.

51. Eugene Staley and Richard Morse, Modern Small Industry for Developing Countries (New York: McGraw-Hill, 1965), p. 47.

COMMENTS BY MELVIN KRANZBERG

The transfer of technology is usually thought of as an imitative process. An underdeveloped nation imports the techniques and tools of industrially advanced countries; or, within a developed nation, one sector of the economy simply adopts a manufacturing process found useful in another; or, within an industry, a firm copies the products and methods of its competitors. These would seem to be simple cases of imitation, were it not that imitation itself is a most complex matter.

All types of change are disruptive of traditional culture patterns, but technological change is perhaps most disruptive of all. For technology involves human work[1] and the ways in which men make their living have a profound influence upon the way they live, their value system, indeed, every facet of their existence.[2] What this means, therefore, is that the transference of technology involves a disruption of previous work habits and thought patterns.[3] In such cases, imitation becomes equivalent to innovation.

Some will undoubtedly demur at my blithe equation of the imitation of technologies with technological innovation. However, recent attempts to introduce imitative products or processes in underdeveloped countries without concomitant changes in other elements of the technological process, or without due regard to existing cultural traits have shown the inability of purely imitative transfer to achieve acceptance or results, unless accompanied by innovative activity in many different areas.[4] Indeed, the major thrust of Dr. Murphy's argument, with which I entirely agree, is that technical change "requires inter-related adjustments" with other factors and variables.[5]

If by transfer of technology we mean the acquisition, development, and utilization of technological products, processes, and knowledge in contexts different from those in which they first developed, we must perforce recognize that such transfer requires innovation within the new context. But, we know from the research

of psychologists and cultural anthropologists that every
innovation--even those narrowly spoken of as economic
or technological innovations--actually has broader inter-
cultural foundations and implications. [6] If we are to
understand the process of technological diffusion, we
must regard technology as a cultural, social, psychological, and political process as well as the imitation
of artifacts.

Professor Murphy discards this sociocultural
definition of technology, claiming that its key variables
are noneconomic in nature. Yet the fact is that many
noneconomic variables enter into economic change.
Indeed, Murphy himself admits this in citing the advantages of his preferred definition--technology as "the
whole process that extends from factor supplies on the
one hand to the marketing outlets on the other"--by
pointing out that this definition deals not only with interrelated adjustments with economic factors, but also
with noneconomic variables before it becomes an oper-
able technological change.

Dr. Murphy then claims that these noneconomic
variables normally change by an evolutionary process
and consequently can be assumed constant for most
economic analysis. This statement is both historically
dubious and mathematically unsound. If our economic
analysis is to be realistic, it must take into consideration the fact that the context is changing, and the use of
differential equations should make simpler the inclusion
of noneconomic variables engaged in constant change.
Technology cannot be separated from noneconomic and
total cultural factors, and Dr. Murphy wisely does not
attempt to do so in his historical case studies.

Each of us has his own way of categorizing the
various factors that enter into technological change,
and, while I might prefer my own, [7] many factors,
which I might enumerate separately, could be sub-
sumed under the four major categories considered by
Murphy; the general rate of economic growth, resource
availability, labor availability, and government action.
Nevertheless, even if we were to give each of these

their widest possible definitions, one factor is largely
omitted from Dr. Murphy's discussion, namely, transportation, which is basic for even the most elementary
industrial life, and a key factor in problems involving
the transfer of technology. [8]   At the very beginning of
the Industrial Revolution, Horner recognized that
transportation was "the hinge upon which the development of industry turned. "[9]

I find also an unproved historical thesis in Dr.
Murphy's assertion that innovations in cotton textile
manufacture took place first in England because "the
artisans of the British clock and watch trade provided
a center for the development and diffusion of new
machines and techniques. " Although the clock-and
watchmakers did provide a background of mechanical
competence in precision machine work, there is no
evidence that the great innovations in textile machinery
came out of the horological trades, nor that they were
specifically influenced by artisans of that craft. [10]

I also detect a certain confusion regarding the
role that governments played in technological diffusion
in the nineteenth century. England's industrial progress
under a laissez-faire policy led Arnold Toynbee to state:
"The essence of the Industrial Revolution is the substitution of competition for the medieval regulations which had
previously controlled the production and distribution of
wealth. "[11] Yet, the Industrial Revolution had its begin-
nings at a time when mercantilist doctrines still determined government policy in Britain, while the great
development of British industry occurred later on under
the system of free competition advocated by Adam Smith.
During the July Monarchy, France consistently manipulated tariffs in an effort to protect infant industries, but
there was no marked industrial progress; under the
Second Empire, a free trade policy was adopted and
French industry flourished. But, was free trade
responsible for the remarkable industrialization of
France during the reign of Napoleon III as much as
the direct state subsidization of transportation networks
and other major technological endeavors?[12]

Sometimes, the mere coming into existence of a state acts as a required impetus for the establishment of industry. Thus, political unification of the German states into the Bismarckian Empire was a precondition for German industrialization during the last half of the nineteenth century, [13] just as the development of a new type of nationalism in Japan cast off the traditional bonds of Japanese society and impelled her to imitate Western technology. Similarily, the recent achievement of independence by many countries in Asia and Africa has made them eager to lay the groundwork for industrialization. [14] The point is that governments must provide a favorable milieu--either by direct action or by being purposefully passive--for technological growth.

Finally, I must take issue with Professor Murphy's conclusion. He claims that "the differences between the world of today and the world wherein modern industrialization began are so significant that the possibility of drawing any real prospects out of retrospect are slim." Whether or not innovations are diffused, adopted, adapted, and integrated into the culture of a people or nation is a matter that is dependent upon a whole complex of interrelated variables. These variables, which are now perceived in today's underdeveloped countries, were also present in the past, even though we did not recognize them until brought face to face with them through our present experience.

However, the mere existence of a number of variables, and the admitted difference between the historical context of the twentieth century and that of two centuries ago, are not sufficient basis for Professor Murphy's pessimistic conclusion that the study of the past has little to offer us today. Far from it! One of the chief developments of the social sciences during the past twenty-five years is our ability to cope with more variables. Instead of throwing up our hands in despair, we should look upon the discovery of these new variables as a challenge to apply our latest techniques--historical and mathematical--to an investigation of these problems. Perhaps the past has more to teach us than Dr. Murphy believes.

NOTES TO COMMENTS

1. Peter F. Drucker, "Work and Tools," Technology and Culture, I (1960), 28-37.

2. A classic statement of "the long arm of the job" is given in Robert S. and Helen M. Lynd, Middletown (New York: Harcourt, Brace and World, Inc., 1929).

3. Ruth Gruber (ed.), Science and the New Nations (New York: Basic Books, 1961).

4. Bert F. Hoselitz, Sociological Aspects of Economic Growth (Glencoe, Ill.: Free Press of Glencoe, Inc., 1960); Jack Baranson, "Economic and Social Considerations in Adapting Technologies for Developing Countries," Technology and Culture, IV (1963), 22-29; Oriol Pi-Sunyer and Thomas DeGregori, "Cultural Resistance to Technological Change," Technology and Culture, V (1964), 247-53.

5. H. W. Singer, International Development: Growth and Change (New York: McGraw-Hill Book Co., 1964).

6. Margaret Mead, "Creativity in Cross-cultural Perspective," in Harold H. Anderson (ed.), Creativity and Its Cultivation (New York: Harper and Brothers, 1939), chap. xiv; Homer Barnett, Innovation: The Basis of Cultural Change (New York: McGraw-Hill Book Co., 1953); Myron A. Coler (ed.) Essays on Creativity in the Sciences (New York: New York University Press, 1963).

7. Melvin Kranzberg, "What Constitutes an Industrial Revolution?" Foreign Policy Bulletin, XXXIX (1960), 113 ff.; Kranzberg, "Voraussetzungen für die Industrialisierung am Beispiel der englischen und französischen Industrie im 18. und 19. Jahrhundert," VDI-Zeitschrift. CV (1963), 14-15.

8.   Wilfred Owen, Strategy for Mobility (Washington, D. C.: Burns and MacEachern, 1964).

9.   H. Horner, An Inquiry into the Means of Preserving and Improving the Public Highways of the Kingdom (London, 1768), p. 8.

10.   Abbott Payson Usher, A History of Mechanical Inventions (Boston, Mass.: Beacon Press, 1959), chap. xi.

11.   Arnold Toynbee, Lectures on the Industrial Revolution of the 18th Century in England (New ed., London, 1928), p. 64.

12.   Rondo E. Cameron, France and the Economic Development of Europe, 1800-1914 (Princeton: Princeton University Press, 1961), Part II.

13.   J. H. Clapham, The Economic Development of France and Germany, 1815-1914 (14th ed., Cambridge: Cambridge University Press, 1936), p. 279.

14.   W. W. Rostow, The Stages of Economic Growth (Cambridge: Cambridge University Press, 1960), p. 26.

COMMENTS BY HENRY H. VILLARD

One may agree with Professor Hagen that society is like a bowl of marbles, no one of which can be moved without changing the position of all the others--or with Professor Murphy's view of "technology" as a process that involves the harmonious meshing of a number of subsystems--yet still wish to be more precise as to what we mean by the marble we call "technology." For, unless "technology" is precisely defined, we cannot decide on its relative importance.

I wish Professor Murphy had given more attention to the role of natural resources. So long as owners of resources sell them freely, I believe the differences in resources availability today account for less than 5 per cent of differences in living levels among developed countries. [1] Even if true today, however, my conclusion may well not have applied in the past, primarily because relatively much higher transportation costs may have significantly increased the importance of resource availability.

Professor Murphy found that government was of little importance in promoting the transfer of technology in the nineteenth century, but believes that it "can play a positive role in technological diffusion." A statement such as this raises, I think, a basic question. Are we approaching the problem of technological transfer as positive scientists describing what has, or may happen, or are we normative developers trying to expedite the development process? Even from a positive viewpoint, I believe that today "so many factors are different that we cannot safely use the past as a guide to the present." But, if we are normative developers trying to expedite development and transfer of technology, the real challenge before us, as I see it, is to create an economy to which the lessons of the past have the least possible application. The one overriding lesson I draw from Professor Murphy's discussion is that the transfer and diffusion of technology is likely to be slow in the absence of conscious efforts to encourage technological change.

Let me illustrate my point with reference to American agriculture. Perhaps we can learn something from the way in which improvements in agricultural technology were transferred and diffused in the nineteenth century, but I doubt whether the past has more than marginal relevance to a present situation, in which government--state and federal--accounts for perhaps 80 per cent of all research expenditures, and spends almost as much again on disseminating research results through our extension service. As a result, productivity in American agriculture has recently increased very rapidly. Yet, Professor Schultz contends "that an economic analysis will show that, while expenditures (on agricultural research) are large relative to past outlays, and compared to what other countries spend for these purposes, the resources committed annually would have to be increased very substantially before the rate of return from this stream of inputs would not exceed that obtained in production activities generally. "[2]

Under such circumstances, not only has the past little relevance, but projections of future spending on research, which basically assume a continuance of present trends, reflect primarily our lack of understanding of the relationship between research and development. At present, perhaps 15 per cent of the one tenth of the national income spent for military production goes for research, amounting to around 1.5 per cent of national income. Moreover, civilian spending on research is concentrated in a relatively small number of "progressive" industries such as electronics, chemicals, or aircraft. Hardly more than 10 per cent of total research spending, amounting to perhaps 0.3 per cent of our national income, is spent for the benefit of sectors of the economy that account for half the national income. If, therefore, more rapid development of the American economy were desired, I believe, the way to achieve it would clearly be to apply the lesson of American agriculture--both in terms of the experiment stations and an extension service-- to the half of our economy where research spending is in effect trivial.

What lessons does this analysis offer for underdeveloped areas, with which we are primarily concerned?
First, I am convinced that, if our objective is to increase
per capita real income, there is no other use of inputs
in any underdeveloped economy which will bring as high a
rate of return over cost as the promotion of birth control--
and no other area where the agricultural lesson regarding
the importance of governmental development and dissemination of improved technology has greater relevance.

Admittedly, birth control is somewhat special,
but I submit that the agricultural lesson has broad application to underdeveloped economies--not merely for
consumer goods such as birth control devices and widely
used technology such as in agriculture, but for most other
areas of the economy as well, though in such areas the
specific procedures may well have to be different.

To sum up in a sentence: The real and over-
whelming need is not to transfer our existing technology
to other countries, but rather to create a new technology
adapted to the needs of the areas of the world we wish to
develop.

NOTES TO COMMENTS

1. Henry H. Villard, Economic Performance
(New York: Holt, Rinehart, and Winston, 1961), chap.
xxxiv.

2. Theodore W. Schultz, The Economic Organization of Agriculture (New York: McGraw-Hill Book Co.,
1953), p. 113.

CHAPTER **2** ECONOMIC THEORY AND
TRANSFER OF TECHNOLOGY

by Jan Kmenta

THE TECHNOLOGICAL GAP

The pool of available technical knowledge consists
of knowledge actually applied in production plus knowledge
that--although potentially applicable--has not been used in
practice. The size of this pool can be referred to as the
"level of technology." This level is considerably higher
for developed countries compared with the underdeveloped
parts of the world; the difference between these levels
constitutes a technological gap. Given that a higher level
of technology implies more efficient utilization of resources,
and therefore higher output, the problem of raising the
level of technology in underdeveloped countries by narrow-
ing the gap, is one of pressing relevance.

However, the definition of the level of technology
should not be confined to applied technical knowledge
only. Some techniques, although feasible, have not been
applied in practice, because they have been considered
"uneconomical" at the prevailing prices of inputs. In
particular, it is quite conceivable that applied technology
in advanced countries has been influenced by labor-saving
considerations, in view of the high price of labor relative
to other factors. [1] However, underdeveloped countries
are likely to look toward capital-saving rather than labor-
saving methods of production, when selecting technology
for industrial application. Thus, technical methods that
are feasible but have not been applied in advanced
countries may well be suitable for application in underdeveloped countries. This points to the appropriateness
of a concept of technology which is not restricted to
practical applications. [2]

A manifestation of the technological gap is given
by comparison of aggregate production functions for a
specific industry or a group of industries in different

countries. The respective production functions are assumed
to be rationally selected, that is, in each country the managers are doing the best they can with what they know. The
technological superiority of Country A ("advanced") over
Country B ("backward") can be demonstrated in one of two
ways. One possibility is that the same quantities of the
same inputs produce a higher level of output in Country A
than in Country B. Such a technological gap may be called
"disembodied." Another way in which Country A may be
technologically superior to Country B is by virtue of the
fact that Country A is using qualitatively superior inputs.
If this is the case, and if the qualitatively differentiated input is capital equipment, then the technological gap can be
described by differences in the "vintage" of the respective
production functions. In such case we can speak of an
"embodied" technological gap, since the technological
superiority of Country A would presumably disappear if
both countries were using qualitatively indistinguishable
inputs.

The technological gap of the "disembodied" kind can
be represented graphically (see p. 41) if we assume that
there are only two inputs, labor and capital, and that the
production function is homogeneous of degree one. [3] We
shall measure the quantity of labor per unit of output ($\frac{L}{Y}$)
on the vertical axis, and quantity of capital per unit
of output ($\frac{K}{Y}$) on the horizontal axis. (Labor is measured
by number of men and capital by number of physical
units.)

The graph shows that, whatever the quantity of
capital (labor), we need less labor (capital) to apply to
it to produce one unit of output in Country A than in
Country B. If labor is relatively expensive in Country A
and relatively cheap in Country B, we should expect the
actual combinations of labor and capital in the two countries to look something like A* and B* shown. The two
curves in Figure 1 depict two levels of technology measured
in terms of unit labor and capital requirements. Applied
technical knowledge would be represented by points corresponding to labor-capital combinations that have been used
in practice, [4] while all the remaining points on or above
Curve A, though feasible, are only theoretical.

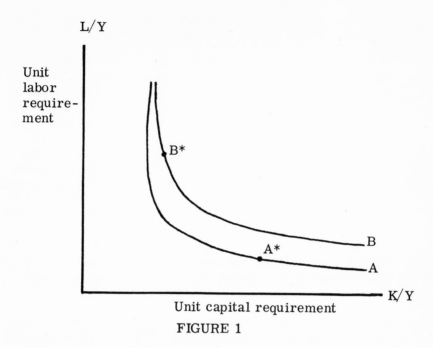

FIGURE 1

THE TECHNOLOGICAL GAP OF
THE "DISEMBODIED" KIND

The extent of the "disembodied" technological gap can be measured with reference to Figure 1 by the distance between the two curves at a particular labor-capital combination, i.e., along a particular ray from the origin. Here we encounter the usual index number problem of whether to take as the basis for comparison the labor-capital ratio of Country A or that of Country B or some third one--a problem which we shall leave aside. Given the specification, we can measure not only the size of the technological gap but also the "bias" of the technological superiority of A over B by comparing the ratio of marginal products as suggested by Hicks. [5] The "embodied" technological gap can be measured simply by the difference in efficiency of the capital equipment used in the two countries.

Having provided a convenient description of the technological gap, we may concern ourselves with changes

in the gap over time.   For this purpose we shall postulate
several different adjustment processes and examine their
implications. [6] Let A_t refer to the level of technology in
Country A at time t, and B_t to the level of technology in
Country B at time t.   One simple relationship between the
levels of technology in A and B would be in the case where
the current level of technology in B is exactly equal to the
level of A several time periods ago.   Mathematically, we
would have

(1) $$B_t = A_{t-L_t} \quad ,$$

where L_t is the number of periods by which B lags behind
A at time t.   We shall call equation (1) above a "simple
lag model. " A useful feature of the model is the flexibility
achieved by allowing the lag to change over time.   In fact,
it is this feature which is indispensable for the introduction
of policy variables.

Since the lag which puts Country B technologically
behind Country A is subject to change, it is of some interest to ask about its determinants.   Unfortunately, there is
no well-developed theory that would provide a straightforward answer to this question, but some ad hoc theorizing
might serve as a starting point.   For inspiration, we may
refer to studies on the transfer of technology concerned
with institutional factors and arrangements.[7] First, we
should realize that not all knowledge lends itself to simple
communication.   Some knowledge cannot be communicated, because it is subject to a patent; other exists in
the skills of labor and cannot be communicated by non-
personal codification, and other still may be embodied in
equipment and instruments from which it cannot be
easily separated. [8] Consequently, any policy measure
to alleviate some of these difficulties of communication
would tend to diminish the technological gap.   Obvious
examples of such measures are laws reducing the protection afforded by patents or removing barriers to
international movements of labor and capital.   A special
mention should be given to the factor of an external
military presence, which is likely to be particularly
helpful in communicating knowledge embodied in labor
and in capital equipment. [9]

Concerning the knowledge that can be communicated without special difficulties, the time-lag involved depends on a number of factors. Foremost of these is likely to be the level of education in the receiving country. This has been recognized by many authors concerned with the diffusion of technology. Richard Nelson, for instance, writes: "The rate at which technological understanding is increased is strongly related to the number of educated people applied to that purpose."[10] Better educated managers are quicker to consider technological change, because they are better able to judge the benefits (and the costs) of the new techniques, and a better educated work force is more adaptable to technical change in production. Another factor, probably associated with the level of education, is income. At low income levels, the exposure to communication of new methods is likely to be considerably less than at high income levels. Factors other than level of education and income are, at least in general, probably less important in accounting for the lag.

The technological gap in the simple lag model is then equal to

(2) $$A_t - B_t = A_t - A_{t-L_t}$$

and

(3) $$L_t = f(z_{1t}, z_{2t}, \ldots),$$

where the z's include institutional variables relating to patents, international movements of inputs, external military presence, etc., as well as the level of education, income, and possibly other explanatory factors. What happens to the gap over time depends not only on the lag L_t but also on the behavior of A_t, that is, on the rate of development of technical knowledge in Country A.

The traditional view of the stock of technical knowledge, for example, in the United States, is that it is simply a function of time.[11] The usual assumption

is that the level of technology advances at a constant rate,
i. e. ,

$$(4) \qquad A_t = A_0 \alpha^t , \qquad (\alpha > 1)$$

where α is a constant equal to the ratio of any two con-
secutive levels of technology. If this is the case, then
the absolute size of the gap is

$$(5) \qquad A_t - B_t = A_0 \alpha^t - A_0 \alpha^{t-L} .$$

Relative to the level of technology in B the gap is

$$(6) \qquad \frac{A_t - B_t}{B_t} = \alpha^{L} - 1 .$$

It is obvious that the relative technological backwardness
of Country B would be reduced if either the lag were
shortened (i. e. , if L decreased) or the rate of growth of
technology in A slowed down (i. e. , if α came closer to
unity). Otherwise, Country B would never "catch up"
with A.

        The assumption of constant rate of growth of
technology in A implies that there is absolutely no limit
to technological progress. A somewhat less optimistic
view is represented by an alternative assumption that
the growth of technical knowledge will slow down and
eventually become negligible. If this is the case, we
might replace (4) by

$$(7) \qquad A_t = k - \frac{m}{t} , \qquad (k, m > 0)$$

where k and m are constants; k is the limit which the
level of technology in A will reach and m determines
the rate of change. Instead of (5), the absolute size
of the gap would be given by

$$(8) \qquad A_t - B_t = \frac{m L}{t(t-L)} .$$

Here, as could be expected, the conclusion is that whatever the lag, the technological gap separating A and B will disappear simply with the passage of time.

A more sophisticated view of the stock of technical knowledge is that it is a consequence of investment, and that the effect of each investment decreases exponentially in time. [12] Then we may write

$$(9) \qquad A_t = \beta \, (I_t + \lambda I_{t-1} + \lambda^2 I_{t-2} + \ldots) \quad (0 < \lambda < 1)$$

or, using Koyck's transformation,

$$(9a) \qquad A_t = \beta I_t + \lambda A_{t-1} \; .$$

Here, I_t represents gross investment at time t in Country A. The technological gap in this case will be

$$(10) \qquad A_t - B_t = \beta \, (I_t + \lambda I_{t-1} + \lambda^2 I_{t-2} \ldots + \lambda^{L-1} I_{t-L+1})$$
$$+ (\lambda^L - 1) \, B_t \; .$$

It follows, then, that the gap will be the greater the higher the levels of recent investments in A, and will be smaller as the level of technology in B becomes higher.

A simple lag model underlying the preceding analysis assumes instantaneous and complete adjustments in the level of technology in B to all changes in the level of technology in A which took place a given number of periods ago. As an alternative, we may consider a model which allows for persistent but only partially successful efforts to close the technological gap. [13] Such a model would be

$$(11) \qquad B_t - B_{t-1} = \rho t (A_{t-1} - B_{t-1}) \quad ,$$

where ρ_t is the adjustment coefficient at time t. Equation (11) can be called a "stock adjustment model." The value of the adjustment coefficient ρ_t lies between

0 and 1; the closer it is to 1, the greater the degree of adjustment of B's level of technology to that of A. The role of ρ_t in the stock adjustment model is very similar to that of the lag L_t in the simple lag model; in fact, the determinants of ρ_t can be considered to be the same as those of L_t as discussed earlier and summarized in (3).

If ρ_t does not change, equation (11) may be solved for B_t to give

$$(12) \quad B_t = (1 - \rho)^t B_0 + \rho [A_{t-1} + (1 - \rho) A_{t-2} + (1 - \rho)^2 A_{t-3} + \ldots + (1 - \rho)^{t-1} A_0] \quad .$$

The dynamic behavior of B_t--and consequently the behavior of the technological gap--again depends on the movement of A_t through time. With a constant rate of growth of A_t [given by equation (4)] the equilibrium path of B_t, say B_t^*, would be

$$(13) \quad B_t^* = [\frac{\rho}{\rho + \alpha - 1}] A_t$$

and the equilibrium gap relative to the level of technology in B

$$(14) \quad \frac{A_t - B_t^*}{B_t^*} = [\frac{\alpha - 1}{\rho}] \quad .$$

This implies that the technological gap could be diminished either by a reduction in the rate of growth of technology in A (α) or by an increase in the value of B's adjustment co-efficient (ρ). If the rate of growth of A_t is presumed to reach an upper limit, as given by (7), then the technological gap will eventually disappear. If the rate of growth of technology in A depends on current and past investments, as in (9), then the technological gap is

$$(15) \quad A_t - B_t = \beta I_t + (\lambda - \rho) A_{t-1} + (\rho - 1) B_{t-1} \quad .$$

That is, the gap depends on current investment (positively) and the level of technology in A during the preceding period. It is interesting that the latter may be negatively related to the size of the gap, providing $\lambda < \rho$, that is, providing B is "learning faster" from A, than A is "learning" from its investment acts.

The two models of adjustment processes discussed in this section represent only a small selection of alternative models that might be considered. They do, however, provide a convenient formal setting for considering the technological gap between advanced and underdeveloped countries and the factors which may influence it. Not surprisingly, both models lead to very similar conclusions, namely, that the gap will be increased by rapid technological development in advanced countries, and will be diminished by greater "adjustability" of the underdeveloped countries.

DIFFUSION OF TECHNICAL CHANGE THROUGH CAPITAL ACCUMULATION

Let us now consider the kind of technical change associated with acquisition and use of capital equipment. Our main concern will be with the case in which technical change is due to, and occurs at the time of, installation of a new piece of capital equipment; technical change following the use of capital equipment will be discussed in the latter part of this section. In either case, technical progress thus conceived, can occur only as a result of gross investment.

Technical progress that occurs at the time of installation of new capital equipment is due to technological superiority of the new equipment. This is demonstrated by a reduction in average cost of production. A question naturally arises as to the absence of universal adoption of technologically superior equipment when this becomes available. More specifically, we wish to know why Country A ("advanced") has capital equipment technologically superior to that of Country B ("backward"). This same question may equally well be asked in connection with the coexistence of firms with modern capital equipment along with the firms using old-fashioned equipment in an

industry within one country at a given time. Whether
technological diffusion is considered nationally or internationally, the reasons for the divergences in the level
of technology used are partly economical and partly non-
economical. [14] They will be considered in turn and in the
context of international transfers.

From the point of view of economic theory, the
appearance of a new piece of capital equipment would
induce firms to replace their old equipment with the new
one only if it were profitable to do so. Replacement will
not be profitable until the reduction in cost due to introduction of new equipment is sufficiently large to pay for
the capital cost associated with the replacement. In other
words, replacement will take place only when the operating
cost of using the old equipment is larger than the operating
cost plus capital cost (including a normal return) involved
in using the new equipment. [15] Availability of technologically superior equipment does not lead to an immediate
scrappage of old equipment, just as the existence of highly
fertile land does not necessarily lead to abandonment of
all less fertile land. In fact, "capital goods in existence
are equally as much a part of the economic environment
as land or other natural resources. Both are gifts: natural
resources are the gifts of nature; capital goods are the
gifts of the past. "[16] This explains, at least in part, the
variety of capital equipment and of the techniques of production used which can be found in many industries within national boundaries as well as internationally.

Consider a manager of a firm in Country B who
finds out about a machine in Country A which, if introduced, would reduce his operating costs of production.
He will replace his existing machine by the new one only
if it is profitable for him. With time, the existing
machine will have shorter and shorter expected dura-
tion, and eventually the profitability condition will be
satisfied. This situation may be now considered from
the viewpoint of the whole industry. Before the new
machine is "discovered," the machines used by different
firms in the industry range in age from very old to
relatively new. The old machines will be the first to
pass the threshold of "obsolescence" and be replaced

by the technologically superior machines. As time goes on, more and more machines will be replaced. Under competition, all firms will be forced to adopt the new machine or incur losses. In the absence of competition, a firm will not be forced into adopting new techniques by the threat of losses, but it will be in the firm's self-interest to do so.

The question now arises as to what determines the speed of adopting the technologically superior capital equipment of Country A by Country B. The answer, from a purely economic viewpoint, is implicit in the profitability condition discussed above. From this, it follows that the adoption will take longer if

    (a) the new capital equipment is not greatly superior to the capital equipment currently in use in Country B;

    (b) the durability of existing machines in B is long;

    (c) the price of the new capital equipment is high;

    (d) the rate of interest in B is high;

    (e) the wage rate in B is low;

    (f) the scrap value of the existing machines is low;

    (g) the industry in B is not very competitive.

In terms of international transfers from advanced to underdeveloped countries, points (c), (e), and (g) are of particular relevance. New capital equipment will normally have to be imported from advanced countries, and consequently its price is increased by the cost of transport and by the amount of duty. Since underdeveloped countries typically suffer from balance-of-payments difficulties, the amount of duty imposed may be high, or import restrictions may apply, or both. The price of

capital equipment may also be boosted by high costs of
repair and maintenance. Further, wages in underdeveloped countries are low, consequently, a high pressure to adjust rapidly to new technology, which requires
less labor, does not exist. Finally, industries in underdeveloped countries are probably not, on the whole, highly
competitive, which diminishes the pressure to lower costs.

In addition, a number of noneconomic factors are
likely to delay the introduction of new capital equipment
still further, if not prohibit it altogether. Most of these
are discussed in considerable detail in the literature on
the diffusion of innovations. They include: social rigidities, and particularly resistance to change in traditional
societies; lack of "economic rationality," implying lack of
desire to maximize profits; incompatibility with institutional
arrangements (e. g., use of large agricultural machinery on
small fields); uncertainty, which tends to increase with the
complexity of the equipment; and several others. The
importance of all of these factors is self-evident and needs
no elaboration here.

A model somewhat different from the one discussed
above is one in which technical change occurs as a result
of "learning." Learning is assumed to be the product of
experience, and in particular to take place as a result of
using capital equipment. [17] The basic relation, inspired
by observations on the production of airframes, is

(16) $$\left(\frac{L}{Y}\right)_N = aN^{-b} \qquad (a,\ b > 0),$$

where $\left(\frac{L}{Y}\right)_N$ is the number of man-hours per unit of output
used with the N-th machine. The implication is that, as
the first machine of a given kind is introduced, it will use
more labor to produce one unit of output than the second
machine, the second machine will use more labor than
the third, and so on. As more machines are introduced,
labor becomes more and more efficient, though at a decreasing rate.

A still different model, linking technical change
to investment, was recently proposed by Kaldor and

Mirrlees.[18] In this model, the rate of growth of output
per worker is assumed to depend on the rate of growth
of gross investment. In this and in other respects, the
treatment of technical change by Kaldor and Mirrlees
is similar to the learning model.

The crucial point, with respect to technical
change that is tied to capital equipment, is that it cannot occur without investment, and, in general, the more
investment the greater the degree of technological progress. The importance of this factor is likely to override
all the other hurdles in international transfer discussed
earlier. This is inevitable, as gross investment is
"... the vehicle of technical progress. ... An economy
with a low rate of gross investment is restricted in the
rate at which new techniques can be brought into use."[19]

DIFFUSION OF TECHNICAL CHANGE
INDEPENDENT OF CAPITAL ACCUMULATION

Some technological progress is achieved without
investment or with very little of it. A classical example
was cited by Lundberg.[20] For a period of fifteen years,
the Horndal iron works in Sweden had no new investment,
and yet output per man-hour rose by over 30 per cent
during the period. Lundberg called this phenomenon the
"Horndal effect." In this case, technological improvement
can be imputed to learning from experience with production. In other cases, technological progress without
investment may be due to new methods of organizing
production (e.g., as a result of time-and-motion study,
or of division of labor), new ways of using raw material
(e.g., replacing simple corn seed by hybrid corn),
better management techniques (e.g., rationalized decision
making), improved quality control methods, and many
others.

Let us first consider technological progress as a
result of experience with production. Suppose the production function for a specific industry in Country A is

(17) $$Y_A = f_A(L, K).$$

The industry is well established in Country A, and Y_A represents maximum output that can be produced with any given quantities of labor (L) and capital (K). Suppose now that the same industry, using the same type of labor and capital, has been in existence in Country B for a relatively short time. The production function in B is

$$(18) \qquad Y_B = f_B(L, \ K),$$

and such that for the same quantities of L and K, say L^* and K^*, $Y_B^* < Y_A^*$. However, with more and more output, Y_B^* will eventually approach Y_A^*. Then we may think of the production function (18) as an "adaptive production function, " and of technological progress as being simply related to output.

If y represents the number of units of output, and $Y^*(y)$ represents the rate of output per unit of time (with quantities of inputs given by L^* and K^*) after y-units of output have been produced, then the "learning process" implies

$$(19) \qquad Y_B^*(y) \geqslant Y_B^*(y-1) \ .$$

Further, following Levy,[21] we may define the "rate of adaptation" as

$$(20) \qquad m = \frac{Y_B^*(y) - Y_B^*(y-1)}{Y_A^* - Y_B^*(y-1)} \ .$$

If m is constant and lies between 0 and 1, equation (19) is formally a model of the "stock-adjustment" type.[22] In this case, the dynamic solution for $Y_B^*(y)$ is

$$(21) \qquad Y_B^*(y) = Y_A^* - [Y_A^* - Y_B^*(0)] \ (1-m)^y.$$

Here $Y_B^*(0)$ is the rate of output in the initial stage of production in Country B. As output y increases, $Y_B^*(y)$ can be expected to approach Y_A^*. In other words, Country B's industry will eventually be nearly as efficient as that of Country A. The length of time needed for a specific industry in Country B to approach, through "learning, " the efficiency of the same industry in Country A, depends on the value of the rate of adaptation m, and on the initial rate of output $Y_B*(0)$. For low values of m, the length of time may be quite considerable.

The adaptive production function provides a convenient framework for considering diffusion of technical change without fixed investment. It appears that growth of efficiency could be accelerated by increasing the rate of adaptation, or by diminishing the initial difference in efficiency, or both. Some of the "speeding up" can be expected to occur simply as a result of experience. Providing that more and more industries which exist in Country A are introduced in Country B, the labor force in B becomes more experienced, and the initial difference in efficiency is likely to diminish, and the rate of adaptation to increase. Further speeding up of the growth of efficiency can be induced--either internally or by appropriate international transfer--by development of industrial engineering (e. g., time-and-motion study, etc.), by increasing the level of education of the labor force (including management), and in many other ways. In fact, the term "technical assistance" may well be defined as assistance by the advanced to the underdeveloped countries in an effort to increase the rate of adaptation in underdeveloped countries.

Another way of promoting technological progress is to improve the skills of the labor force--by what has been termed "investment in humans." Since skilled labor is scarce in underdeveloped countries, it is rather expensive. This has two possible implications.

The first implication is relevant in the case where it is possible to substitute workers of different skills. The underdeveloped countries will select those techniques of production that use more unskilled and less skilled labor. But, since at least some of the technical progress in the advanced countries tends to have a labor-saving bias, and since the labor saved is largely unskilled, the benefits from technical progress would be smaller in the underdeveloped than in the developed countries. For example, the increase in efficiency may be due to the application of time-and-motion study, which may be possible if an industrial engineer is on the staff. The employment of the industrial engineer may save the work of, say, ten unskilled workers. But, if the wage of the industrial engineer is higher than that of the ten workers combined, it does not pay to make the change.

The second implication arises when it is not possible to substitute unskilled for skilled workers. In this case, the choice of techniques available to the underdeveloped countries is severely restricted. Thus, the speed with which the underdeveloped countries may draw on the benefits due to technical progress in the advanced countries will be reduced to the speed with which the underdeveloped countries improve the skill-mix of their labor force.

From the point of view of international transfers, the scope for improving the level of technology in underdeveloped countries by raising the skill of labor is substantial. It may consist of overseas training of workers from the underdeveloped countries, establishment of educational and vocational exchange programs, temporary or permanent "import" of skilled workers from other countries, training programs through "external military presence," and similar efforts. There are, as a rule, very few formal institutional barriers to transfers of this sort, but there may exist social and political inhibitions which may prove to be a hindrance.

NOTES

1. See J. R. Hicks, The Theory of Wages (New York: St. Martin's Press, 1963), p. 125.

2. Throughout the chapter we are assuming that there are no appreciable differences in the product mix between the countries to avoid complications due to demand-determined choice of techniques. Such complications would, for instance, exist if consumers in one country had a considerably stronger preference for handmade articles than the consumers in another country.

3. A similar graph was used for a somewhat different purpose in W. E. G. Salter, Productivity and Technical Change (Cambridge: The University Press, 1960), p. 22.

4. In each country there are, of course, firms which operate above their respective curves. Under competition these firms could exist only in the short run; in our scheme they are not considered.

5. Hicks, op. cit., p. 120.

6. The following analysis draws on R. R. Nelson and E. S. Phelps, "Investment in Humans, Technological Diffusion and Economic Growth" (Cowles Foundation for Research in Economics at Yale University, Discussion Paper No. 189, August 12, 1965). The authors examine adjustment processes with respect to the pool of inventions and the pool of applications.

7. See, for example, J. Baranson, "Transfer of Technical Knowledge by International Corporations to Developing Economies," American Economic Review, LVI (May, 1966), 259-67; J. N. Behrman, "Foreign Investment and the Transfer of Knowledge and Skills," U. S. Private and Government Investment Abroad, ed. by R. F. Mikesel (Eugene, Oregon: University of Oregon Books, 1962); D. L. Spencer, "An External Military Presence, Technological Transfer, and Structural Change," Kyklos, XVIII (1965), 451-74.

8. For an elaboration, see I. Svennilson, "The Transfer of Industrial Know-How to Non-Industrialized Countries," Economic Development, ed. by K. Berrill (New York: St. Martin's Press, 1964).

9. On this point see Spencer, op. cit.

10. R. R. Nelson, "Aggregate Production Functions and Medium-Range Growth Projections," American Economic Review, LIV (September, 1964), 591.

11. This is how technological progress is introduced into a production function in a large number of studies. For a leading article see R. M. Solow, "Technical Change and the Aggregate Production Function," Review of Economics and Statistics, XXXIX (August, 1957), 312-20.

12. This view was put forward by Haavelmo and is described in K. J. Arrow, "The Economic Implications of Learning by Doing," Review of Economic Studies, XXIX (June, 1962), 155-73.

13. See Nelson and Phelps, op.cit., p. 8.

14. See Salter, op. cit., chap. iv.

15. For a lucid and extensive discussion, see Salter, op. cit.

16. Ibid., p. 61.

17. See Arrow, op. cit. Our version is somewhat different from Arrow's, since he assumes that the learning takes place in effect only in the capital goods industry, and that no learning takes place in the use of a capital good once built. We assume just the opposite.

18. N. Kaldor and J. A. Mirrlees, "A New Model of Economic Growth," Review of Economic Studies, XXIX (June, 1962), 174-92.

19. Salter, op. cit., p. 63.

20. Described in Arrow, op. cit., p. 156.

21. F. K. Levy, "An Adaptive Production Function," American Economic Review: Papers and Proceedings, LV (May, 1965), 386-96.

22. The adjustment process implied by (19) is the same as that considered earlier in connection with the difference in the stock of technical knowledge in A and B. [See equation (11).] Here, we are concerned with adaptation to a given and unchanging production function.

COMMENTS BY EDWIN MANSFIELD

Jan Kmenta has written an interesting study on a difficult and important topic. Whether the models he discusses are sufficiently rich to provide significant insight into the very complex problems of international transfer of technology is debatable. But this is due primarily to the lack of previous work in this area and to the complexity of the problems. As Kmenta points out, the area has long been neglected.

Kmenta begins by defining the technological gap between two countries as the distance between their unit isoquants (assuming constant returns to scale). Employing a "simple lag model," which assumes that the level of technology in Country B is equal to that in Country A, L periods before, he analyzes the behavior of the technological gap, given that technology in Country A increases at a constant rate, or that it is proportional to an exponentially weighted moving average of previous investment rates. He also considers a partial adjustment model, which assumes that the change in Country B's level of technology is a certain fraction, ρ, of the existing technology gap between Countries A and B. Again, it is a simple matter to analyze the behavior of the technological gap, given that technology in Country A increases at a constant rate or that it is proportional to an exponentially weighted moving average of previous investment rates.

It is useful to apply these models--some of which are standard fixtures in other areas of economics--to the transfer of technology. But it seems to me that they deal only with a minor part of the problem of explaining the size and behavior of the technological gap, since they investigate only the effects of the speed of adjustment on the gap, taking the speed as given. In effect, the problem of explaining the size and behavior of the technological gap is exchanged for that of explaining the size and behavior of the speed of adjustment, and I am not sure that the latter problem is much easier than the former. Kmenta does devote a few paragraphs to the determinants of the speed of adjustment, pointing out that it depends on the importance of patents and other such barriers to the transfer of technology, as well as on the level of education in the receiving country. An equally important factor is the social system and attitudes toward technical change in the backward country, the relevant attitudes being those of the people as a whole as well as the government planners. Another important factor is the size of the technological gap, which influences the costliness of the transfer. Also, the rate of adjustment obviously depends on the extent of the resources devoted to promote technological transfer--a variable which is ignored.

International differences in technique do not necessarily imply a technological gap. Nonetheless, it is interesting to investigate the factors determining the rate of international diffusion of various techniques. Kmenta lists the factors influencing how rapidly the operating cost of using an older type of equipment will exceed the operating cost plus capital expenditure of the new. Assuming that the new equipment will replace the old when replacement reduces costs, these factors will determine how rapidly the new technique will spread. It is interesting to note that Maddala and Knight, in their recent study of the international diffusion of the oxygen steel-making process, find that a simple economic model of this sort is of little use in explaining the observed diffusion process. For example, although the oxygen converter is more economical than open hearths, at least three new open-hearth furnaces--and no oxygen converters--have been ordered in Mexico since 1962.[1] Conventional cost comparisons are likely to be of more use in explaining the rate of diffusion of an innovation within the United States, than in accounting for international differences in the rate of diffusion.[2] The latter seem to depend heavily on social rigidities, planning lags, and other noneconomic factors.

Finally, Kmenta makes use of learning curves and adaptive production functions to represent the behavior over time of the input-output relationships in the two countries. As elsewhere in the chapter, he

makes no attempt to analyze the various kinds of technological transfer required to narrow the technological gap,
the ways of effecting such transfer, or the costs of
doing so.   Regarding various kinds of technological
transfer, it is important to distinguish between the transfer of general information--how to read blueprints or run
a lathe--from specific information acquired by a firm as
a consequence of its having produced a certain product,
or of its having invented certain processes or products.
It is also important to identify the various ways in which
technology can be transferred.   Data can be transferred
in the form of books, blueprints, patents, etc.; people
can move, taking information with them; or reverse
engineering[3] can be carried out.   Each type of information presents different problems insofar as transfer is
concerned, and each way of transferring information
differs in cost and effectiveness.

The transfer of specific information gained
through experience with a particular process can probably
be analyzed most effectively in terms of the standard
learning curve, one of the most interesting questions
being: To what extent can learning be transferred from
a firm in one country to a firm in another country? An
interesting study of this question was carried out by
Hall and Johnson, who looked in detail at the transfer
of the F-104J fighter to Japan. [4] They concluded that
technology was easily transferred for about 60 per cent
of the plane, transferred with difficulty for about 20 per
cent, and the technology for about 20 per cent was not
transferred at all.   The lack of general technology in
particular areas was a principal reason for difficulty
of transfer.   With regard to the airframe, it appears
that considerable learning was transferred from Lock-
heed to Mitsubishi.   That is, the man-hours required
to produce the first Japanese F-104J's were appreciably
less than the number required to produce the first
American F-104J's.

NOTES TO COMMENTS

1. G. Maddala and P. Knight, "International Diffusion of Technical Change--A Case Study of the Oxygen Steel Making Process (Stanford University, 1965; Mimeographed).

2. For some studies of the rate of diffusion within the United States, see my "Technical Change and the Rate of Imitation," Econometrica, XXIX (1961), 741-66, and Research, Innovation, and Technical Change (New York: W. W. Norton and Co. , 1966).

3. Daniel L. Spencer, "An External Military Presence, Technological Transfer, and Structural Change," Kyklos, XVIII (1965), 455, passim.

4. G. Hall and R. Johnson, "Aircraft Co-production and U. S. Public Policy (Rand Corporation MSS, 1966).

CHAPTER 3 THE SCHUMPETERIAN THEORY AND CONTINENTAL THOUGHT

by Edgar Salin*

SCHUMPETER'S THEORY

Statics, Dynamics, and Growth

Schumpeter's theory is based upon the distinction between statics or circular flow and dynamics. However, he uses these terms differently from J. B. Clark or from modern usage. In Schumpeter's statics or circular flow, the economic agent behaves in a purely conventional and traditional way. The author follows, in all respects, the common view that the factors of production are combined only by experience. The economic agent at this stage is absolutely colorless.

In an early review, Professor von Beckerath[1] has observed that The Theory of Economic Development[2] shifts from a description of a purely theoretical state, more and more, toward a description of a certain historical period. Reading the chapter on statics, the reader perceives the contours of the antique Oikenwirtschaft (household economy) or the medieval Fronhofswirtschaft (manorial economy) behind Schumpeter's descriptions.

Schumpeter's statics serves two different purposes at the same time; it describes the basic state of things, and it serves as a contrast to dynamics.[3] [It can, therefore, equally be described by the absence of the innovating entrepreneur, who is defined as the economic agent introducing new combinations of factors of production.] Though Schumpeter is influenced as much by J. B. Clark as by the mathematical school (Walras, Pareto), his concept of statics is substantially different, since his

---

* The author is greatly indebted to Dr. Bruno Frey for his helpful assistance.

circular flow is not in equilibrium in any mechanical sense
but rests in the sociological surroundings. [4] Therefore,
statics does not exclude growth or evolution of the factors
of production, and does not necessarily represent a
stationary state. [5]

Dynamics or development is characterized by the
appearance of the innovating economic agent, called
entrepreneur, who arranges new combinations of factors
defined, in Schumpeter's terminology, as technical progress. These innovations shake the foundations of the
prevalent static state of the economy, and eventually
start an upswing of the business cycle. The upswing
is strengthened by a following hoard of imitating entrepreneurs until the system again reaches a static, but
not necessarily stationary, equilibrium.

Growth in Schumpeter's system means only the
increase in the physical factors of production, especially
labor and real capital. Thus, growth is distinctly different from development or evolution. [6] This continuous
growth of resources is not Schumpeter's object of study,
since he maintains that it is not "the prime mover of
economic change"; indeed, compared with development,
growth is of minor quantitative importance. [Investments
are largely induced by profits, which often result from
innovations. Hence, "growth, but especially saving,
owes its actual quantitative importance to another factor
of change without which its modus operandi in the capitalist world cannot be understood. " [7] Therefore, growth
cannot produce the fluctuations which interest Schumpeter most--business cycles can be understood in an
economy without growth, but not vice versa. The equilibrium of static circular flow includes growth, because
the continuous small increase in factors of production
allows the economic agents to use their past experience
as an adequate guide; they are not forced to introduce
new combinations of factors suddenly.

In order to clarify these concepts, Perroux
distinguishes three states: statics in the strict sense,
quantitative dynamics, and qualitative dynamics. [8]
Statics in the strict sense involves constancy of the

factors of production and constancy of their combination.
Quantitative dynamics includes the adaptations to continuous change in the factors of production, while qualitative dynamics is characterized by the introduction of
new combinations of factors by the innovator. For
Schumpeter, one very important difference between
statics and dynamics lies in the fact that a positive rate
of interest exists only in a dynamic economy, i. e. , a
positive rate of interest is a direct effect of innovations
or technical progress; this proposition has stimulated
a most heated debate, which cannot be pursued here. [9]

Invention and Innovation

Schumpeter makes a very sharp distinction
between invention and innovation. Inventions have no
immediate economic significance, since they can be
fructified only by entrepreneurs, who are able and
ready to find new combinations of factors. Therefore,
inventions play a minor role in the Schumpeterian
theory. He believes that there exists always a reservoir of technical inventions, which is inexhaustible,
and which is growing continuously. [10] Innovations in
Schumpeter's sense are the application of inventions
by entrepreneurs to increase economic productivity.
Innovations are the cornerstone of Schumpeter's
theory, since they not only explain the business cycle,
are the cause of positive profits, and of a positive rate
of interest, but also because they define the role of the
entrepreneur. Economic development is synonymous
with technical change.

Innovations, in contrast to inventions, appear
discontinuously. They tend to be introduced near
equilibrium, where the risks are at a minimum. There
is a very slight connection, therefore, between inventions and innovations, because inventions do not stimulate innovations. [11] Consequently, in order to explain
the process of innovation, Schumpeter starts from
static conditions, from a constant population, constant
political and social organization, and so forth, [12]
because it is only the burst of the innovating

entrepreneurs that pulls the economy out of the circular flow into development.

The process of innovation can be generated by five different classes of events:[13] by the introduction of a new product, by a new method of production, by the opening up of a new market, by the conquest of a new source of supply of raw materials, and by a change in the organizational structure of any industry. While all these events involve discontinuous change in the combination of factors of production, "the introduction of new commodities... may serve as the standard case."[14] This concept of technical progress is much broader than the notion that is commonly used in modern theory. [15] The motives of the innovating entrepreneurs differ greatly, and, possibly with exception of the desire for profit, are largely of a sociological and psychological nature, for example: "The will to conquer, the impulse to fight, to prove oneself superior to others, to succeed for the sake... of success itself..."[16] Schumpeter's entrepreneur, who innovates, at least in part, for innovation's sake, can be compared with the Marxian capitalist, who accumulates for the sake of accumulation. [17]

Technical change is always connected with real capital accumulation in new firms and new plants, by "new men";[18] it opens up new investment possibilities not only in the innovating but also in connected industries. [19] Thus, it is evident that Schumpeter lays much more importance on the conception that innovations open up new investment possibilities rather than the opposite, stressed in modern theory, namely, that capital investments induce innovations.

The Entrepreneur[20]

The appearance of innovating entrepreneurs brings the circular flow into a movement of development. The concept of innovating entrepreneur, often called the Schumpeterian entrepreneur, has left a great mark on European and American writers, and the discussion has not ended. In this respect, the

works of Werner Sombart and Max Weber apparently have
a more lasting influence. Although Schumpeter describes
the entrepreneur in a manner   which Max Weber considers "ideal - typical, " Schumpeter foresees the vanish-
ing of the entrepreneurial function.[21] A change in the
context of the entrepreneurial function is quite evident
in Europe, but cannot generally be seen in the United
States.[22]

CONTINENTAL CRITIQUE
OF SCHUMPETER'S THEORY

No attempt is made to present a comprehensive
review of the Continental critique of Schumpeterian
theory; however, the thoughts of four scholars provide
a representative sample.

Erwin von Beckerath

Reviewing Schumpeter's work, Beckerath attacked
one particular aspect of his theory, namely, the explanation of the appearance of the innovating entrepreneurs, a
subject which was also discussed in the United States.[23]
Schumpeter begins his explanation of the sudden burst
of entrepreneurial innovation in static equilibrium with
the assumption of stationary economy, because the
innovating act is not a consequence of the surrounding
economic factors.   In later chapters, Schumpeter points
to certain "favorable outside conditions" stimulating
the appearance of innovators, and therewith   reduces
somewhat the importance of the spontaneous bursting
of the entrepreneurial innovation.   This, however,
does not invalidate the Beckerath   critique:

> At decisive points, the theory shows
> an incorrect picture of reality, as the
> appearance of entrepreneurial performance
> can, in principle, never be understood at
> all; it cannot even be analyzed if changes
> in the data of the 'milieu' are not presup-
> posed. . . . The real factors must be ripe

before certain acts of the spirit
and of the will, i. e., entrepreneurial actions, can unfold. In
my opinion, it would be logically
incorrect to overlook these conditions. It is an abstraction which
goes too far, and which does not do
justice to intrinsic parts of the
problem. [24]

Von Beckerath and Schumpeter differ significantly
in their assumptions about the nature of the economic
progress. Whereas according to Beckerath, economic
progress, in its deepest sense, cannot be explained by
economic factors, Schumpeter believes that it can. Consequently, Schumpeter does not attempt to explain the
entrepreneurial activity objectively by the occurrence of
external events. [25]

Francois Perroux

Perroux concentrates his critique on the following
points. First, Schumpeter shifts from the very few
pioneering entrepreneurs, who by definition are rare, to
the great mass of imitating entrepreneurs, and is convinced that both represent the same type of economic
agent fulfilling similar functions. In the opinion of
Perroux, these two types of economic agents are qualitatively so different that they must never be identified
by the same name. [26]

Second, Schumpeter wanted to achieve two goals
at the same time in his statics, a functional theory, and
a historical description. Perroux feels that he did not
succeed, because historical description of a static
economy necessarily must be characterized by a well-
determined set of institutions. He demonstrates and
proves his criticism by the example of income distribution which, under a purely functional conception of
circular flow, cannot be explained without paying attention to the authority. [27]

Perroux's main criticism is, however, that Schumpeter attempted to explain too much by the one single phenomenon, the innovation. [28] He goes so far as to say: "Schumpeter has not provided us with a theory of capitalistic evolution, but rather with a theory of re-arranging things in a new way. "[29] Therefore, the general impression of Perroux is that the positive teaching of Schumpeter's theory was and is much less influential than the suggestion it evokes. [30] Perroux comes to the conclusion that this theory is less useful as a whole than in the defenses, precautions, and con-cessions, which the author is forced to make in his exposition. [31]

Walter Adolf Jöhr

In Jöhr's Business Cycles, the Schumpeterian system is treated separately, under the heading: "Exo-genous Business Cycle Theories. " In this voluminous book, Jöhr makes numerous references to Schumpeter's but mainly he repeats the same aspects of Schumpeter's theory of innovation and the role of the entrepreneur. [32] This seems typical of most writing on Schumpeter in Continental literature.

Jöhr is inclined to answer in an affirmative sense the question whether the burst of technical prog-ress in the upswing is not just the reflection of business cycle movements, because the upswing generates con-ditions more favorable to economic success than any other phase of the cycle. [33] He discusses two hypoth-eses which attempt to explain the burst of innovations by entrepreneurs. One is the well-known interpreta-tion of Kuznets, according to which Schumpeter "expects high entrepreneurial ability to pause after the innova-tion and descend to the lower level of its imitators... but this implies cycles in the supply of entrepreneurial ability. "[34] Such a hypothesis is rejected by Jöhr, since it comes too near to psychological explanations of the cycle. Another hypothesis seems to him at least as problematic as the first one. This hypothesis states that the technical progress by innovating entrepreneurs

transforms the economic interdependence so deeply no
other creative entrepreneur can hope to be successful
until the economy has adapted to the preceding innovation. [35] In the opinion of Jöhr, the explanation drama-
tizes the innovating act too much, because it turns all
other entrepreneurs into imitators. [36] Thus, Jöhr comes
to the conclusion that Schumpeter's theory can only be
accepted if one starts from an irregular appearance of
innovations, which is not at all unlikely. Though there
is some overlapping in the whole economy, which
reduces the variation in success of innovation, it does
not level it out completely.

Jürg Niehans

Niehans starts from a very different point of
view, since his main object is to find a quantitative
measure of technical progress. He characterizes
Schumpeter's theory as a "magnificent, but. . . non-
binding historical painting" which, because it cannot
be quantified, is committed to failure. [37] It must be
added that Schumpeter was well aware of this short-
coming. [38] However, the problem of quantification has
become very important to economists as they attempt to
integrate technical progress into economic theory. [39]

SCHUMPETER AND THE MODERN THEORY
OF TECHNICAL PROGRESS

Concept and Definition of Technical Progress

At first sight, Schumpeter's definition of technical progress or innovation is very similar to, and as
abstract as, that in use by the modern economic theory.
He states that the production function

> ...describes the way in which the
> quantity of product varies if the quan-
> tity of factors vary. If instead of
> quantities of factors we vary the form
> of the function, we have an innovation. ...
> Therefore, we will simply define

innovation as the setting-up of a new ·
production function. [40]

It must be remembered, however, that Schumpeter describes innovation as including five different classes of
events. If one compares his concept with the current
use of the term "technical progress" in Europe, [41] which
goes back to R. M. Solow's most influential empirical
article[42] of 1957, then it becomes quite evident that
Schumpeter's "new combination of factors of production"
includes more than Solow's definition. [43] Nevertheless,
as Schumpeter considers the introduction of new products
to be the standard case, the essential part of both definitions of technical progress is the same. [44]

This is as far as the formal definition of technical
progress goes. The content seems to be quite different.
Although the Solowian definition of technical change includes "process innovation" and "product innovation,"
both can be reduced to "less inputs and the same output"
or "more output with the same inputs." This is purely
formal; however, the definition fails to capture the
essence of product innovation. [45] It is only now that
economists are trying to relate the creation of new
products to welfare consumption and economic growth. [46]

One reason why the modern theory of technical
change neglected this problem lies in the fact that development of the index number of new goods creates unsur-
mountable difficulties; i. e. , how should a new product
be weighted? The quantity of the new product cannot be
compared to any former quantity, since this product did
not exist before. Most economists concentrated their
attention on quantitative measurement of the importance
of technical progress, and left this problem aside. For
a long time, technical change was simply considered as
the residual factor in empirical research. At this
point, the objection of Niehans comes into its own right:
Schumpeter's theory of technical progress cannot be
tested empirically, because of the index number problem
connected with the creation of new products.

Modern Theory of Technical Progress
on the Continent

A review of the current literature on the economics
of technical change reveals two main characteristics.
First, there is a very strong influence of Anglo-American
writers who follow R. M. Solow. Today, there can be
found an extremely vast body of literature on the formal
aspects of technical change, e. g. , the discussion of
Harrod's or Hicks'neutrality is as lively in Europe as in the
United States and England. In result, the concept of technical change has gained a great deal in precision, which
is particularly important for growth theory, but the increase in precision had to be paid for by a loss of content.
Such very important problems as the transfer of technical
progress from invention to innovation, and other problems
of product innovation, are barely treated at the macroeconomic level. [47]

Second, the most important feature of Schumpeter's
innovations, namely, their discontinuous appearance is no
longer accepted today. Technical progress is considered
as an essentially continuous, regular phenomenon, and an
autonomous function of time. Alternatively, it is an induced
function of investment, the technical progress function of
Kaldor, [48] or of accumulated production, as in models of
the learning-by-doing type. [49] In both these cases, even
the induced part of technical change is not subject to
sudden bursts, which view is reinforced in the current
golden-age models. Two reasons may account for the
strong preference of economists to regard technical progress as continuous. First, they think that recurring
bursts of innovations at the microeconomic level even
out at the macroeconomic niveau. Second, for a purely
practical reason, it becomes mathematically much more
difficult to treat sudden discontinuous bursts of technical
change. One immediate result of this assumption of the
regularity of technical progress is that the distinction
between invention, which grows in Schumpeter's system
more or less continuously, and innovation is blurred,
because now both are supposed to increase continuously.

Continental Treatment of Technological Transfer

There are only few works available which deal
with the various stages between invention and innovation.
Niehans in an article, which was written before Solow's
pathbreaking empirical research, has typically distinguished five stages of technical progress: increases in
basic knowledge, applied science, construction technique
(in which the known basic elements are constructed into
marketable products), production technique (i. e., processes of mass production and sales organization), and technique of use. [50] But Niehans does not describe how the
stages interact with each other, what are the time-lags,
by what factors they are conditioned, and so forth.

Third, after World War II, French economist,
Jean Fourastié, wrote a very important and influential
book, Le Grand Espoir du XXe Siècle, one of the first
works which, after Schumpeter's, is really concerned
with technical progress. [51] I do not intend to deal with
this book at length, because a very similar approach has
been made in the United Kingdom by Colin Clark in books
and articles which are readily accessible and known to
American readers. [52] Fourastié deals not only with the
differential impact of technical progress on sectoral
labor productivities and on sectoral employment differences, but also with technical progress in general. But,
Fourastié did not clearly visualize the question of the
transfer of technology as a component of progress. He
comes very close to the problem, however, when he
writes:

> In effect, the technological progress
> would be the same for all nations, if it
> were only the result of scientific advance-
> ment, because science is a part of the
> public domain. [53]

Fourastié discusses financial, economic, and human factors responsible for the discrepancy between technical
and scientific progress. But these obstacles account
rather for the differences between sectors of the economy

in the application of technical change and do not explain
the general transfer problem. The second part of the
sentence, quoted above, seems to indicate that Fourastié
assumes scientific knowledge, i. e. , invention, to be
readily available and evenly distributed amongst all
economic actors and nations. By that assumption, he
denies the important role of information about technological and scientific possibilities in the transfer process.

An English Contribution

Contrary to Continental thought, English economists seem to have realized that it is necessary not only
to advance knowledge of the formal aspects of technical
change, but to conduct empirical research on this problem.
A few remarks on the study dealing with The Sources of
Invention and on the transfer of invention will be presented
here.[54]

The authors differentiate between several stages
in the process of technological transfer; namely, pure
science directed towards understanding, and technology
directed towards use. Under the heading of technology
goes invention as well as development: "Invention is
something which comes before development. The essence
of invention is the first confidence that something should
work, and the first rough tests that it will, in fact, work. "[55]

Jewkes' conclusions as to the relations between the
stages are based on a great many case studies. In general,
the comments are very careful because of the extremely
wide range of possibilities encountered. Thus: "It is not
known whether there is necessary connection between the
growth of scientific knowledge and the growth of technology
and invention or, if there is a connection, what are its
laws. "[56] As to the development of inventions, the authors
are extremely doubtful whether it is more rapid than in
former times, as is often contended today:

> Is it in fact true that nowadays inventive
> ideas are more quickly seized upon and
> exploited and their potentialities more

swiftly diffused throughout the community?
We do not know because these things cannot
be measured in their totality . . . . Because
this cannot be measured, it is seductive to
reach snap generalizations based on a few
spectacular illustrations. [57]

The authors observe correctly that one of the
reasons for growth of research in firms is that it improves
the connection between invention and innovation.   The scientist working in a firm is subjected to the same discipline
and shares the same loyalties as the firm's other members.
This is only one aspect of the fact that in the transfer from
invention to innovation, technical considerations give way
gradually to market considerations, and that, today, market considerations seem to intrude further into the sphere
of invention and scientific research.

SCHUMPETERIAN THEORY
AND TECHNOLOGICAL TRANSFER

After indicating that a good deal of criticism is
possible and necessary against some points, and even
against the basis, of Schumpeter's theory, what can we
still learn from him?   The basic point of his approach,
namely, that the process of invention is distinct and
separate from the process of innovation, is and remains
right.   Recently, an author explicitly confirms this point
without mentioning Schumpeter, when he writes:

When it comes to new products
rather than incremental improvements
in products or processes, we see most
clearly the point that invention is not
enough. Given an invention. . . substantial obstacles may still remain. [58]

Naturally, the subject is open for discussion about what
those nonincremental new products and production processes are, but it does not seem to be justified to say that all
innovations are incremental, and that, therefore, Schumpeter's analysis does not apply.

The same author, in his informative article, brings forward another notion, seemingly without being aware that it is again a Schumpeterian notion; i. e. , the pool of knowledge of new possibilities which "are always present abundantly accumulated by all sorts of people. "[59] And Rosenbloom phrases ". . . there is the feeling that a vast pool of underutilized technology has been created by these massive (military and space) R & D programmes. "[60]

Schumpeter's description of how the very pioneering entrepreneurs apply an invention to practical use, and how, after a certain time-lag, other entrepreneurs follow until the innovation is generally accepted, is quite realistic. [61] This vision accounts, however, only for one of the two important time-lags involved; namely, between the first adaptation of an innovation until the general acceptance by a majority. It does not explain the time-lag between the emergence of an idea, or invention, and its use as an innovation.

Schumpeter reasoned only on the assumption that minor and major innovations entail new plants, new firms, and new men. [62] He knew quite well that in dropping this assumption, "a great part of the theoretical scheme which we are going to use would have to be modified. "[63] But this assumption is today so obviously unrealistic that his theoretical analysis, thereby, is severely invalidated. [64] Nowadays, it is the established large corporation which is innovating, [65] and its managers who are rising to the top through a hierarchial process--not new men. [66] However, Schumpeter foresaw in his last book, Capitalism, Socialism and Democracy, the concentration and organization of research in large corporations, which, in turn, diminishes the importance of the entrepreneurial function. This notion, however, does not help much in the actual analysis of technological progress, because the general facts are more or less known, and because more empirical research and evaluation are needed. Thus, Schumpeter's work is most effective when it is used for the progressive understanding of the whole process of technical change. In this sense let us recall

Schumpeter's own wish:

> The younger generation of economists
> should look upon this book merely as some-
> thing to shoot at and to start from--as a
> motivated program for further research.
> Nothing at any rate would please me more. [67]

NOTES

1. Erwin von Beckerath, "Gedanken zu Schumpeter's Theorie der wirtschaftlichen Entwicklung, " Schmol-
ler's Jahrbuch, LIII (1929), 537 ff.

2. Joseph A. Schumpeter, The Theory of Economic
Development, trans. R. Opie (Cambridge, Mass.: Harvard University Press, 1949).

3. Beckerath, op. cit. , p. 196.

4. Francois Perroux, La Théorie Pure de la
Dynamique Capitaliste (Paris: 1935), reprinted in F.
Perroux, La Pensée Economique de Joseph Schumpeter,
Les Dynamiques du Capitalisme (Geneva: 1965) p. 62.

5. Ibid. , p. 66; Irma Adelman, Theories of
Economic Growth and Development (Stanford, Califor-
nia: Stanford University Press, 1961), pp. 95-96;
Richard Clemence and Francis Doody, The Schumpe-
terian System (Cambridge, Mass.: Addison-Wesley
Press, 1950), p. 27.

6. "... we shall designate by the term (positive or negative) growth, changes in population
(strictly also changes in age distribution and the sum
total of savings plus accumulations).... That term is
to emphasize not only variations in both those variables that are continuous in the mathematical sense...
but also that it occurs at a rate which changes but

slowly. " Joseph A. Schumpeter, Business Cycles (New York: McGraw Hill Book Company, 1939), I, 83.

7.   Ibid. , p. 84.

8.   Perroux, op. cit. , p. 136.

9.   Perroux goes so far as to say: "The main point is that of eliminating interest in Statics. " op. cit. , p. 67.

10.   Joseph A. Schumpeter, Capitalism, Socialism, and Democracy (3rd ed. , New York: Harper and Bros. , 1950), p. 118.

11.   "The social process which produces invention and the social process which produces innovation do not stand in any invariant relation to each other. " Schumpeter, Business Cycles, I, 86.

12.   Beckerath, op. cit. , p. 201 ff.

13.   Schumpeter, The Theory of Economic Development, p. 66.

14.   Schumpeter, Business Cycles, I, 84.

15.   See pp. 68 ff.

16.   Schumpeter, The Theory of Economic Development, p. 93.

17.   Adelman, op. cit. , p. 101.

18.   Schumpeter, Business Cycles, I, 93 ff.

19.   Clemence and Doody, op. cit. , p. 16.

20.   Edgar Salin, "Der Gestaltwandel des europäischen Unternehmers, " in E. Salin, Lynkeus, Gestalten und Probleme aus Wirtschaft und Politik (Tübingen, Germany: J. C. B. Mohr, 1963), XII, 228-39; Edgar Salin, "European Entrepreneurship, " Journal of Economic

History, XII (1952), 366 ff.; Edgar Salin, "Manager" in
E. von Beckerath et al., Handwörterbuch der Sozialwissenschaften (Stuttgart,Germany: G. Fischer, 1961) VII, 107;
reprinted in Salin, Lynkeus, XII, 240-48.

21.   Max Weber, Die Protestantische Ethik und
der Geist des Kapitalismus (Tübingen, Germany: J. C. B.
Mohr, 1934).

22.   Salin, "Der Gestaltwandel des Europäischen
Unternehmers, " p. 238.

23.   Erwin von Beckerath, Lynkeus, Gestalten
und Probleme aus Wirtschaft und Politik (Tübingen,
Germany: J. C. B. Mohr, 1962), VII, 185-202; Simon
Kuznets, review of Joseph A. Schumpeter's Business
Cycles, in American Economic Review, XXX (June,
1949), 257 ff.

24.   Beckerath, Lynkeus, op. cit., pp. 201-2.

25.   Ibid.

26.   Perroux, op. cit., p. 147. "It is impossible
to apply the same name--without causing confusion--to
both types of economic agents: the very few whose main
characteristic is the innovative (pioneering) effort, and
the more numerous whose essential characteristic is
imitation. "

27.   Francois Perroux, Les Trois Analyses
de l'Evolution et la Recherche d'une Dynamique Totale,
pp. 199-200. "We do not hesitate to state that J.
Schumpeter, to our best knowledge, has failed in his
basic attempt to present a stationary flow, which is
functionally pure and historically correct. "

28.   Ibid., p. 234.

29.   Perroux, La Théorie pure..., p. 189.

30.   Ibid., p. 190.

31. Perroux, Les Trois Analyses..., p. 234.

32. Walter Adolf Jöhr, Die Konjunkturschwan-kungen (Tübingen, Germany: J. C. B. Mohr, 1952).

33. Ibid., p. 182.

34. Kuznets, op. cit., p. 257 ff., p. 263.

35. Jöhr, op. cit., p. 182.

36. "Such theory is similar to a war doctrine that would ascribe all victories in the world history to the accomplishments of one single hero." Ibid., p. 183. Jöhr certainly goes too far in this statement.

37. Jürg Niehans, "Das ökonomische Problem des technischen Fortschritts," Schweizerische Zeit-schrift für Volkswirtschaft und Statistik, XC (1954), 145-56. "The inability to quantify was the reason why Schumpeter's hypothesis of an economy driven by the engine of entrepreneurial ideas became colorful and grandiose, however, at the end, an historically doubt-ful picture. This, as the author himself seems to realize, deprived his life work of final success." (P. 147.)

38. Schumpeter, Business Cycles, I, 88.

39. See the next sections.

40. Schumpeter, Business Cycles, I, 87.

41. Alfred E. Ott, "Produktionsfunktion, tech-nischer Fortschritt und Wirtschaftswachstum," in J. Niehans, G. Bombach, and A. E. Ott, Einkommens-verteilung und technischer Fortschritt (Schriften des Vereins für Socialpolitik, Gesellschaft für Wirtschafts- und Sozialwissenschaften, Neue Folge, Vol. XVII [Berlin: E. Schneider, 1959]); English translation in International Economic Papers, XI (1962).

42. Robert M. Solow, "Technical Change and the Aggregate Production Function," Review of Economics and Statistics, XXXIX (1957), 312 ff.

43. Alfred E. Ott, "Technischer Fortschritt," in E. von Beckerath et al., Handwörterbuch der Sozialwissenschaften (Stuttgart, Germany: G. Fisher, 1959), X, 302-16.

44. Schumpeter, Business Cycles, I, 84.

45. This refers especially to end products going directly into household or government consumption as e. g., the automobile. Technical change in intermediate products is at the same time, product innovations on the selling side, and process innovations on the buying side.

46. A German economist writes: "...presently, the rapid change in products is an immediately recognizable fact. Nevertheless, it is excluded from the majority of growth theories..." K. Borchardt, "Die Veränderlichkeit der Konsumgüterstruktur in der wachsenden Wirtschaft," in Theorien des einzelwirtschaftlichen und gesamtwirtschaftlichen Wachstums (Berlin: 1965), p. 113; see also: Dan Usher, "The Welfare Economics of Invention," Economica, XXXI (August, 1964), 279-87.

47. Such articles as e. g., W. R. McLaurin, "The Sequence from Invention to Innovation and its Relation to Economic Growth," Quarterly Journal of Economics, LXVII (1953), 97 ff., do not seem to exist in German economic literature. In three recent doctoral dissertations on the economics of technical change (which usually cover a wide range, and use an enormous amount of literature), one can find no treatment at all of the transfer problem of invention to economic use: Florian Fleck, Untersuchungen zur ökonomischen Theorie des technischen Fortschritts (Freiburg, Switzerland: Universitätsverlag, 1957); Hans Krieghoff, Technischer Fortschritt und Produktivitätssteigerung (Berlin: Dunker & Humblot, 1958); Joachim Häusler, Die ökonomischen Folgeerscheinungen des technischen Fortschritts (Berlin: 1960).

48. Nicholas Kaldor, "A Model of Economic Growth," Economic Journal, LXVII (December, 1957), 519-624.

49. In such models, past production (or investment) is said to confer knowledge upon the worker at the machine, which results in increased productivity. K. J. Arrow, "Economic Implications of Learning by Doing," Review of Economic Studies, XXIX (June, 1962), 155-73; F. K. Levy, "An Adaptive Production Function," American Economic Review, Papers and Proceedings, LV (May, 1965), 386-96.

50. Niehans, "Das ökonomische Problem des technischen Fortschritts," pp. 149-50.

51. "Here we do not consider capital as the fundamental factor in contemporary economic evolution. We simply consider it as a servant of progress." Jean Fourastié, Le Grand Espoir du XXe Siecle (Paris: Presses Universitaires de France, 1949), p. 4.

52. Colin Clark, The Theory of Economic Progress (London: Macmillan Company, 1940).

53. Fourastié, op. cit., p. 33.

54. The aspect of imperfect information is stressed, for example, in John Jewkes, David Sawers, and Richard Stillerman, The Sources of Invention (London: Macmillan Company, 1958), p. 257. "The market for new inventive ideas is imperfect.... Firms looking for new products to purchase often hardly know where to begin their search. Inventors wishing to sell ideas often have not the faintest notion which firm may be interested in them."

55. Ibid., p. 17.

56. Ibid., p. 6.

57. Ibid., pp. 236-37 The text goes on: "On the
other side, however, it may be asked whether there is
much cause for self-congratulation in the fact that although a jet-propulsion plane flew in 1939, in 1956 there
was not one type of aircraft flying commercially with jet
engines and only one with turbo-propeller engines? Or
that color television is still available only in one country?"

This seems to be true in Germany too. There
are many indications that the time between the invention
and its industrial use has lengthened in recent years,
especially for major innovations. The General Manager
of one of the largest chemical firms in the world, BASF
(Badische Anilin- und Sodafabrik A. G. , Ludwigshafen),
mentioned in his address for the centenary of the firm
some very interesting facts. It took the chemists of
the firm only a few years to master technically the
synthesis of ammonia (around 1910); it took the firm 18
years (1880-97) to find a technical solution for the synthesis of indigo, but it took more than 100 years to
produce and to use the acetylene gas. [Carl Wurster,
Die BASF-- 100 Jahre im Dienste des Lebens (Ludwigshafen am Rhein: 1965).]

58. Richard S. Rosenbloom, Technology Trans-
fer-- Process and Policy (Washington, D. C. : National
Planning Association, 1965). For a very interesting
analysis of the transfer problem of military technology
based on Japanese experience compare: Daniel L.
Spencer, "An External Military Presence, Technological Transfer and Structural Change, " Kyklos, XVIII
(1965), 451-74.

59. Schumpeter, The Theory of Economic
Development, p. 88.

60. Rosenbloom, op. cit. , p. 6.

61. Alfred E. Ott is of the same opinion in his
"Technischer Fortschritt, " in Handwörterbuch der
Sozialwissenschaften, X, passim.

62. Schumpeter, Business Cycles, I, 93 ff.

63. Ibid.

64. Perroux, in his foreward to La Pensée Economique de Joseph Schumpeter, Les Dynamiques du Capitalisme, writes: "Today, we interpret the innovation differently from the past; we see it as emanating from science and research, stimulated and even organized by the governments; we are forced to follow its real paths of diffusion, which are not Schumpeterian at all..."

65. Edwin Mansfield, "Entry, Gibrat's Law, Innovation and the Growth of Firms," American Economic Review, LII (December, 1962), 1023-51; Mansfield, "The Speed of Response of Firms to New Techniques," Quarterly Journal of Economics, LXXVII (May, 1963), 290-311; In German: Horst Albach, "Zur Theorie des wachsenden Unternehmens," in Theorien des einzelwirtschaftlichen und des gesamtwirtschaftlichen Wachstums (Berlin: 1965).

66. Salin, "Manager," op. cit.; Salin, "Der Gestaltwandel des europäischen Unternehmers," op. cit., passim.

67. Schumpeter, Business Cycles, I, p. v.

COMMENTS BY ALEXANDER GERSCHENKRON

I should like to add a few elaborations to Professor Salin's lucid and illuminating chapter. My intention is to concentrate primarily on the historical locus of Schumpeter's theory, and--even more briefly--on the problem of empirical verifications of some of its aspects. I feel that the problems involved have an important bearing on creation, diffusion, and transfer of technology.

Schumpeter himself was, of course, quite aware of some historical limits of his interpretation. His concern was with modern economic development, and the kingpin of the theory--the innovating entrepreneur--in the context of his analysis was viewed as a phenomenon of modern economic history. In fact, as Professor Salin rightly says, Schumpeter perceived not only the rise but also the decline of the entrepreneur, even though his phrasing "obsolescence of the entrepreneurial function" was somewhat misleading. For what has been in fact happening has hardly been a decline in the rate of innovations, and/or in the rate of emergence of new combinations of factors of production. The function--the specific entrepreneurial function--is still exercised, and perhaps performed better than ever before; as it is, e. g. , when one of the great corporations in the United States maintains, in addition to its regular research division, what they call a "dream division, " in which serious and persistent work on potentially most momentous innovations is being conducted. What is different is that the connection between invention and innovation becomes particularly intimate under these conditions and, as Schumpeter clearly pointed out, the social resistance to innovation is reduced. The heroic quality of the entrepreneurial activity no longer exists to any comparable extent. That quality played a large role in Schumpeter's thinking. At times he would indeed speak of the rationalist and antiheroic features of entrepreneurial performances. The entrepreneur, he would say, was just a drop in the competitive sea.

But essentially Schumpeter's entrepreneur is equipped
with some romantic traits. He has some resemblance
to the medieval knight errant, who rides out in search
of exciting adventures, ready to slay the dragons of
routine and stagnation. It is probably true that this
image of the entrepreneur made it much easier for
Schumpeter to accept, and acquiesce in, the social and
economic framework of his time. Accordingly, the
change in the carriers of the entrepreneurial function--
its institutionalization rather than obsolescence--filled
him with dismay and nostalgia. This, however, is only
of parenthetic interest in the present context. More
important is the fact that, even before the more recent
changes occurred, the entrepreneurial function over
historically important areas and periods did not quite
correspond to the Schumpeterian image. It contained
some specific institutional elements, which curiously
enough are closely connected with an aspect of Schumpeter's theory that has not been touched upon in Professor
Salin's chapter. I am referring to Schumpeter's concept
of capital, and to the specific role assigned to the banks
in the process of economic development.

Schumpeter's capital is capital disposition, i. e.,
additional claims against national income that are created
ad hoc by the banks and passed on to entrepreneurs, who
use them to bid productive resources away from previous
employments, and in this way are likely to start processes of forced savings. In this sense, credit creation is
an integral part of Schumpeterian theory. As such, it
has certain similarities with Marx's concept of original
accumulation of capital, and Schumpeter mentions
several times that precapitalistic accumulations of
wealth may be regarded as an alternative to credit
creation. Like Marx, Schumpeter does not make it
quite clear that stress on either method of financing
implies essential discontinuity in the process of growth,
at least in any realistic consideration of the process.
The main point, however, is that from a realistic,
that is, an historical point of view, the role of the banks
as agents of economic development can be seen as a
function of the degree of economic backwardness of the
individual areas--let us call them countries--on the eve
of their spurt of economic development.

What matters in an historical inquiry is, of course, not whether banks and their credit creating activities were present at all or altogether absent. History seldom operates with absolute contrasts. Rather, the question is, under what conditions the role of the banks can be reasonably regarded as a strategic factor in the process of development. And the answer to that question should be given along the following lines: In a country with a rich and successful premodern economic history, previous accumulations plus current accumulations by entrepreneurs were likely to constitute a sufficient reserve for the capital dispositions needed. In very backward countries, the inclemency of the social climate effectively impeded the operation of a credit system. Thus, the countries standing between the two extremes became the geographic locus for the convincingly verifiable application of Schumpeter's theory; except that countries in which, because of great backwardness, the capital disposition was provided in a different way, gradually, as their backwardness diminished, came into a position in which banks began to play the role of the strategic factor in the further process of development. Thus, countries did grow into the Schumpeterian model in the very process of development. But they also tended to grow out of it. For even in countries of intermediate or medium backwardness, the time came when the development had proceeded so far that capital dispositions for further growth and development in Schumpeterian terms were obtained from entrepreneurial profits, and the entrepreneurs no longer depended, to any comparable extent, on the credit creation of the banks.

Here, however, an additional point must be made. In the area of "medium backwardness," and during the heyday of the banks as an engine of economic progress, the role of the industrial entrepreneur was not quite as decisive as Schumpeter believed it to be. The innovating entrepreneur was not the sole source of innovations. For it would represent a fatal underestimation of the role of banks, in the period of their maximum significance, to see them as nothing more

than a source of capital disposition for the entrepreneur.
The fact, a most important historical fact, is that the
banks--taking the investment banks in Germany or Italy
as a paradigm--inserted themselves vigorously into
innovational activities. Time and again, one finds that
the Schumpeterian entrepreneurial function was split,
or rather exercised conjointly, by the entrepreneur and
the men in charge of the financial institutions, and in
many cases it would be extremely difficult to say who
had the original creative idea, or who was primarily
responsible for a given innovation. That was perhaps
the strongest and most interesting impression I received
scrutinizing the archives of the Banca Commerciale for
the period between the middle of the 1890's and the beginning of World War I.

        Furthermore, since Professor Salin's chapter
deals with the transfer of technology, let me add that,
to a large extent for the reason mentioned, the banks
played an essential part in the process of international
borrowings of technology. In fact, the process begins
with the spread of the banks. As one appraises the
history of German investment banks, one cannot help
feeling that what was being created there, this new
form of banking, was in itself one of the most powerful
economic innovations, perhaps comparable in its
importance with the application of steam power to
production of goods and services. The German
banks spread to Italy and initiated the great spurt
of Italian industrial development; in itself a case
of technological borrowing of formidable significance.
This use of the term "technological" may transcend
the current vocabulary. However, it was only natural
that Italian enterprises, working under financial and
entrepreneurial tutelage of the banks, imitated many
elements of German technological progress, and
every such imitation, equally naturally, contained
much genuine innovational adjustment to the different
environment. The history of investment banks,
particularly in Central Europe, is also a history of
diffusion and transfer of technology. To be aware of
those considerations does two things: It establishes
and expands the significance of Schumpeter's ideas

and, at the same time, delimitates the area and period
of historical application of important elements of the
theory.

Let me just add a few comments on the problem
of quantification of Schumpeter's theory. It is undeni-
able that the difficulties in this respect are great. The
reason does not lie simply in the index number problem.
The fact (mentioned by Professor Salin) that new commodities emerge in the course of development, and that
the yardstick we use to measure the rate of change
expands and contracts in the very process of measurement is a general difficulty, which is not peculiar to
Schumpeter's model. More important, I believe, is
the fact that statistical measurement of forced savings
processes, which are specifically ex ante, cannot be
readily carried out from ex post data; to say nothing
of the fact that reliable data are hard to come by. But
this does not mean that significant elements of theory
cannot be tested at all. And, indeed, this is precisely
what Erik Dahmén tried to do for Sweden in his monu-
mental study on Swedish industrial entrepreneurship. [1]
He succeeded fairly convincingly in isolating first the
progressive industries from those that were stagnating
or regressive, then proceeded to divide the progressive
industries according to the presence of what he called
market-filling or market-creating activities, and then
to associate the latter either with the introduction of
new commodities or new methods of production.
Following Schumpeter's train of thought, he then tried
to separate "new" and "old" enterprises, and to relate
his findings to the previous classification regarding
innovations in progressive industries. The result is
that Schumpeter's suppositions or intuitions did not
stand up too badly with respect to new commodities,
which were handled to a considerable extent, although
not always introduced, by new enterprises. And the
hypothesis failed, more or less, with regard to new
methods of production. Here, old industries were
the main seat of innovating activities, and continued
to dominate the market in the products resulting
from the application of the new methods. Thus,
Schumpeter's idea that innovations were mostly

launched by new men in new enterprises did not hold for
Sweden of the interwar period. And Schumpeter's
"secondary wave, " the imitative spread of innovations--
the transfer of technology within the economy--could be
ascertained with considerable clarity with regard to
new commodities, but much less so with regard to new
methods. It should be noted that Dahmén's data refer
to the interwar period in Sweden, and as such, they are
less conclusive as far as the historical validity of Schumpeter's theory is concerned, or its application to earlier
periods. It may well be that Dahmén's work indicates
temporal boundaries of Schumpeter's model, which are
additional to those mentioned earlier. But, at the same
time, Dahmén once more illustrated the wealth of ideas
contained in Schumpeter's theory, the stock of exciting
questions to be addressed to the material, and the
operational character of such questions. It is hoped that
Dahmén's work will find followers among economic historians, who should be eager to carry out similar tests
with respect to other countries and other periods. There
is little doubt that in this way much additional light can
be shed on the processes of transfer of technology both
within the individual countries and across the international
boundaries.

NOTE TO COMMENTS

1. Editor's note: Erik Dahmén, Svensk Industriell
Företagarverksamhet, with English summary, (2 vols.;
Stockholm: Industriens Utredningsinstitut, 1950).

COMMENTS BY SERGE-CHRISTOPHE KOLM

Professor Salin's chapter, concentrating on recent Continental thought, is a valuable approach to appraisal of the contribution of Schumpeterian theory in relation to the transfer of technology to developing nations. Both the theory and reaction against it stem from an attempt to apply the Schumpeterian framework to policy problems, in which mainly European countries have been involved. However, Continental thought and experience in transfer of technology apply more generally to world-wide conditions.

The development of Continental thought may be seen in four stages. First, there was a great heritage on the diffusion of techniques problem, derived essentially from Schumpeter, and also the similarly majestic approaches of other scholars, one of the most famous being Francois Perroux. Second, five or six huge practical policy problems arose after World War II, but the mentioned theories proved to be nonoperational and unable to guide policy choices. Then, there followed an endeavor to create more direct, practical, and useful tools of analysis. Lastly, those tools have been applied both in Europe to receive American technology, and to transfer European technology to former colonial countries.

A brief discussion will follow of some useful points and shortcomings of the majestic approach to the transfer of technology, when used as a guide to policies, especially in development problems. The useful points remaining from Schumpeter's theory were essentially: emphasis on innovation and entrepreneurship; the concept of discontinuous growth instead of smooth growth, since the former is a much more genuine approach to the development process than the latter; the importance of credit facilities to the entrepreneur, i.e., the financial requirement of innovation. On the other hand, Schumpeter's theory presents several shortcomings which impair its usefulness with limit interest in theory. For one,

invention, innovation, and the speed of imitation are
determined exogeneously, and, therefore, are not
explained by the framework of Schumpeterian theory.
For another, Schumpeter's contention that the risk
of enterprise is not borne by the entrepreneur, but
by the capitalist lender, seems to be seriously challenged. Although only the lender incurs the risk of
failure of the enterprise, most aspects of the outcome
of the undertaking are both uncertain and vital to the
entrepreneur, and therefore the outcome is risky for
him. Several specific empirical studies of the causes
of lack of innovation in rural underdeveloped zones
have pointed out the risk situations and uncertainty as
the most important blocking factors. In still another
point, Schumpeter's theory is lacking in detail, and
is too historically oriented to be useful for policy
choices. Finally, Schumpeter's monism, i. e.,
his attempt to force everything down to a single
explanatory element is, as any such effort, still at
the hypothesis stage, and although aesthetically
attractive, scientifically dangerous.

In the last fifteen years, several problems
compelled European economists to develop comprehensive analyses, and to build more operational tools
of transfer of technology. First, there are lessons
drawn from the surprising rapidity of recovery in
the postwar period, regardless of massive destruction of capital, though technical knowledge was
largely spared. Second, the appearance of the
Common Market induced competition between technologically heterogenous firms and branches, as
did the establishment of technologically more advanced
American firms in Europe. The growing importance
of the public and semipublic sectors in some Western
European economies, combined with the fact that in
these countries most research is government supported, raised the innovative propensity of civil
servants and government agencies. Finally, within
the framework of national planning, governments
became concerned with diffusion of technology.
The French plan is called a "Plan for Productivity, "
and consists of sectoral "Commissions of Modernization. " However, the most interesting development

in the postwar period is the change in relations between European countries and their colonies, relations which are presently characterized by a growing concern for the development, as opposed to mere exploitation or "presence keeping," of these underdeveloped areas.

The most bitter experience of this attempt at development appeared early. Soon, it became evident that transportation, power, irrigation, social overhead, pilot farms, and so forth, were in most cases, insufficient per se to raise native production. Inadequate transfer of technical know-how emerged as the usual bottleneck. In response to this gap, a new tool, development management analysis, was originated, which combines a socio-ethnological approach with the modern tools of operations research, in order to find the best way of transferring technical knowledge.

A brief review of considerations underlying the preparation of the first development plan for Senegal between 1958 and 1960 provides an interesting illustration. The central problem was the allocation of scarce resources to several possible processes in order to diffuse technological knowledge; the formal structure of the planning process was activity analysis. The scarce resources included: people with some basic training (primary teachers, soldiers, veterans, skilled workers, and so forth) able to learn quickly, and to participate in spreading of the techniques; funds from national or foreign sources, though the availability of funds was related to the process chosen; political support by the government.

Five possible channels for spreading technology were selected for analysis: the existing administrative structure; the political parties; the traditional social structure; a specially created agency, "Development Corps," incorporating schools, youth movements, and social workers; the newly established entrepreneurs, well-provided with credit. With the assistance of these five possible channels, the transfer of technology would be effected mostly by imitation. In the agricultural sector, productive processes under consideration defined

clearly the possible outcome of the analysis. Depending
on the region, the productive process was either harrowing with oxen and donkeys instead of harrowing by hand,
or cultivation of transplanted instead of nontransplanted
rice, and so forth. Some of these improved techniques
could easily multiply family incomes by three times or
more.

All future outputs were, of course, uncertain.
The activities differed by the uncertainty, time pattern,
and nature of the output mix (production, scholarization,
and hygiene, etc.), by the input coefficients, and by
their effect on the distribution of wealth and power (for
which the government's preferences and values were
used). The optimal processes and channels varied by
regions, because of both differences in ecology, and
a huge range in the traditional social structure. It is
of special interest that neighboring component states
of the Republic of Senegal chose to emphasize different
social processes and channels in otherwise similar
regions. Study of the outcome already seems to allow
us to draw some conclusions about the choices made.

This only serves to show one possible approach
to the problem of the transfer of technology, which I
find probably more useful than the majestic approach
of academic scholars. The interest in the latter, however, enables a policy-oriented social scientist to
decide on a choice between a Schumpeterian diffusion
process by innovation, demonstration effect and imitation, and technological transfer by teaching, persua-
sion, and/or coercion.

CHAPTER **4** THE SOCIO-ECONOMIC VARIABLES

by Bert F. Hoselitz

The day before yesterday we followed un-
consciously what was called Nature; yesterday we tried conscientiously to conform to
"nature"; but today, our power having grown
considerably, it behooves us sometimes to
protect nature and sometimes to arrange it
in ways which seem favorable. We have
somehow become responsible for evolution. . .
a reality is to be constructed and not events
awaited.
--Gaston Barger[1]

Unfortunately, mankind has not yet accepted, or
perhaps even understood, the responsibility for increasing
knowledge and technical capacity, which the passage of
time has forced upon it. Traditionally, Western thought has
divided the history of mankind into approximately three
periods.[2] Initially, human society progressed with little
recognition of the scientific basis for that progress. Even
after the transition from a paleolithic to a neolithic culture,
somewhere around 8000 or 9000 B.C., when man first
learned to domesticate crops, his capacities were improved
very little; he was still ignorant of his technical and economic powers. However, this transition does mark the
period during which man began to learn first crude, and
later more sophisticated, skills from his elders.

The second great transition occurred some 4,000
to 6,000 years later, the urban revolution. With the
development of cities came the development of politics,
metal-working, the wheel, and other examples of advancing technology. (Regretfully, we must also add to the list
of inventions during this period, war, slavery, and the
exploitation of others.) At this point, man followed where
science and technology led him, with little or no effort to
control his progress. After 3000 B.C., the first great

political communities learned to use their advanced
agricultural knowledge to establish great empires--
Greece, Rome, the European communities north of
the Alps--and, in fact, could not have done so without
the advance in agricultural technology they had achieved.
These empires could not exist   unless at least a portion
of the population they controlled   produced more
than it needed to survive, in order to provide food for
those who lived in the cities.   And when the political
power holding these empires together disintegrated, the
empires themselves could not survive.

Even at this stage, less than 3 per cent of the
world's population lived in cities, and yet this miniscule
proportion of the population was responsible for what
we think of as "history." The peasants continued to
produce more or less the same crops in more or less
the same way, no matter what "power" happened to
dominate them; something "new" was incorporated into
their meager technological store only decades or even
centuries after its introduction. The system was dependent only upon a few inventions, which had taken place in
various areas, and had spread slowly through the rest
of the world.

From the sixteenth century on, inventions became much more frequent, representing a fundamental
increase in the rate of growth of knowledge within a
small scientific subculture in Western Europe. It was
preceded by a slow cumulative increase in what might
be called popular knowledge and popular technology--
the kind acquired in the ordinary business of life and
in the pursuit of ordinary occupations, the kind whose
origins are lost in prehistory.

It becomes easier to trace the growth of knowledge, skill, and productivity after the fall of Rome in
the West, and after the time of the Han Empire in the
East. In the eighth century, water wheels were invented,
and the horse was introduced to stirrups and a horse
collar. In the next 300 to 500 years, man discovered
the rudder, the windmill, the clock, and the compass.
The Chinese were the technological leaders, followed
by the Islamic Empire from 1200 to 1400.

Our Western-oriented education gives us a very distorted view of world history. We fail to realize that during most of the Middle Ages our ancestors lived on an obscure peninsula, somewhere near the edge of the civilized world. Today, there exists a large body of students of Chinese history and economics who are trying to find out why the take-off in rational science did not occur in China. The historical reasons why it did not are not yet clear.

But, from the seventeenth century on, the third great transition in the growth of knowledge was achieved. Such great names as Copernicus, Kepler, Galileo, and Newton had a tremendous impact in Europe, and were a major factor in the creation of European power and its extension over the whole world.

Nonetheless, another 200 years passed before the scientific revolution affected the economic and social life of the mass of the population. Assuming that the founding of the Royal Society of Science in London in 1660 marks the beginning of the scientific revolution, it was not until the middle or late nineteenth century that major industries began to be dependent on technological knowledge. The steam engine, for instance, was developed in a practical form late in the eighteenth century, but did not come into extensive use until almost a century later, after the development of the theory of thermodynamics around 1840. The development of the textile industry, often associated with the industrial revolution of the eighteenth century, owed very little to the pure science. The inventions that made possible rapid expansion of textile industry, such as the spinning jenny, were no more complicated than a medieval clock-- they were merely extentions of a technology characteristic of the Middle Ages.

Perhaps the best mark of the beginning of the true technological revolution is the invention of the aniline dyes, resulting from the development of a new chemical principle, in the 1860's. After that, certainly, major steps based upon new scientific discoveries came thick and fast. Extensive use of electricity would be

inconceivable without the findings of Michael Faraday
and later, of the James Clerk Maxwell equations about
1870, just as the present prospects for broad use of
nuclear energy would have been impossible before the
work of Bohr and Einstein; already we can foresee the
initiation of vast achievements on the basis of recent
biological and medical advances.

In economically developed countries, such as
the United States, Australia, or Sweden, it is impossible
to estimate industry's scientific base with any accuracy--
perhaps three-fourths of their modern industry could
not have been established without pre-existing scientific
inventions and developments. Today, these economically
developed nations constitute a separate class. The distinction is not only between high and low rates of productivity, but also between an industry and agriculture based
principally on scientific foundations, and an industry
and agriculture left far behind.

Many of our contemporaries speak of "two different
worlds, " and in some ways, this is true. The national
income per capita in the United States is already about
$3, 000, and there is no reason to assume that it may not
progress to $5, 000 or even $10, 000 within the lifespan of
our children.

But have we truly arrived at a different age?
Will mankind's knowledge expand to the point that scientific achievement is taken for granted? In my opinion,
the answer is no, for two reasons. First, the rate of
growth of scientific advance is no higher today than it
was, for example, in the late nineteenth or early
twentieth century. In the United States, the proportion
of Gross National Product going into private research
and development has stabilized at around 2. 4 per cent
in recent years. Also, the total number of patents
issued annually has remained very much the same,
even though the distribution of patents between individuals and corporations has shown a distinct shift over
time.

Second, for the next 100 years at least, [3] the
great majority of the world's population will experience
little benefit from the scientific advances of the developed
countries. In 1960, the developed countries accounted
for 854 million people, and the underdeveloped for 2, 136
million, or 28. 6 and 71. 4 per cent, respectively. Assuming that present rates of population growth prevail to the
year 2000, of the total world population of 7, 410 million,
1, 393 million will live in developed countries and 6, 017
million in underdeveloped, or 18. 8 and 81. 2 per cent,
respectively. Thus, in the next thirty-five years, three-
fourths to four-fifths of the world's population will live
in countries that are unlikely to achieve anything like
the present rate of innovation in the United States.

Table 1 offers data on several measures of
innovation in the United States in recent years. The
early years are marked by rapid rates of expansion,
in terms of investment in research and development
and of the number of researchers employed. Growth
was apparently slowed by World War II, but recovered
very quickly, achieving a high rate in the 1950's. In
current dollars, the outlay rose from $2. 1 billion in
1950 to $9. 5 billion in 1960, an annual gross rate of
expansion of about 16 per cent, or almost three times
that of Gross National Product (6 per cent). The number
of scientists and engineers grew from roughly 150, 000
to 800, 000 in the same period, compared to a growth in
total labor force of one-eighth.

But projections for the decade of 1960 to 1970
do not repeat these rapid rates of growth. Dollar outlay
is expected to rise by only 6 per cent annually, compared
to a Gross National Product growth of 4 per cent, while
the number of research employees is expected to grow
by 400, 000. Even though dollar outlay will almost double,
the number of research workers will not follow, because
salaries can be expected to rise about 20 per cent or
more. The proportion of research workers in high-
salaried brackets may go up, and the percentage of
research workers in the total labor force may grow.
By 1970, barring any new innovations with tremendous

TABLE 1

RESEARCH EXPENDITURES AND RESEARCH PERSONNEL IN THE UNITED STATES, 1920-70[a]

Year	Expenditures (millions) Actual	Expenditures (millions) Equilibrium[c]	Equilibrium rate of expenditures (% of GNP)	No. of research employees	Civilian Labor Force[b] (millions)
1920	48	-	0.05	7,367	40,282
1931	214	-	0.28	32,830	45,480
1940	336	-	0.33	70,033	47,520
1946	1,190	-	0.56	138,500	-
1947	1,600	2,500	1.1	-	-
1948	1,900	2,600	1.0	-	-
1949	1,900	1,900	0.74	-	-
1950	2,100	2,600	0.92	165,032	59,975
1951	2,400	3,100	0.94	187,000	-
1952	2,700	3,400	0.98	232,000	-
1953	3,400	4,800	1.3	-	-
1954	3,800	4,700	1.3	440,000	-
1955	4,300	5,500	1.4	-	-
1956	6,000	9,900	2.4	-	-
1957	7,200	9,800	2.3	618,600	65,011
1958	7,900	9,700	2.3	-	-
1959	9,000	11,600	2.4	-	-
1960	9,500	10,800	2.2	780,000	73,126
1970	18,000	18,000	2.4	1,180,000	-

a. Data are from Yale Brozen, "Trends in Industrial Research and Development," Journal of Business of the University of Chicago, XXXIII (July, 1960), 205-6; "The Future of Industrial Research," ibid., XXXIV (October, 1961), 440. Sources are given in the articles.

b. U.S., Bureau of the Census, Historical Statistics of the United States, Colonial Times to 1957 (Washington, D. C.: U.S. Government Printing Office, 1960), p. 70.

c. Editor's note: The meaning of equilibrium as used here is within the context of the articles by Brozen.

impact on the economy, we may expect private research and development expenditures to reach 2. 4 to 2. 5 per cent of Gross National Product.

But   is this a temporary or permanent plateau? In my belief, it is a permanent one. We experienced a rapid and unusual increase in research expenditures in the last forty or fifty years. Nevertheless, the research industry, if we may call it that, is much nearer an equilibrium than it was in 1950, and this equilibrium position will move much slower in the future than it did in the past, for the following reasons: The great surge in government-financed research, particularly in industrial laboratories related to defense research, is tapering off; the expansion in numbers of research personnel has reached a diminishing comparative advantage, in terms of alternative opportunities; the point is approaching where research productivity will fulfill the demand for new techniques; and the tax changes that favored an increase in research and development expenditures in 1954 are not likely to be repeated.

A listing of the succession of industries that benefited from the rapid expansion of research and development expenditures is probably not important. In the 1940's, the primary beneficiaries were aviation, fabricated metals, and electrical equipment; they have continued to enjoy research and development advantages in recent years, but also have the raw materials industries, and later the space-related industries.

What is more important is the fact that the demand for research personnel was greater than the supply during the period from 1920 to 1950. As can be seen from any Sunday edition of The Chicago Tribune, there is still, in all probability, a shortage of such personnel. But we can expect that the 1970's will see demand and supply balanced in this regard-- additional expansion is not in the offing. Statistics from other countries apparently uphold the view that research and development expenditures will tend to stabilize at this level.

Our apparent ability to support research and
development activities at the level of $18 billion a year
leaves, of course, a leeway with regard to the question,
which field of research progresses more quickly in any
given year. Biology or space research may come to
dominate the field, for example, while textiles, wood
products, petroleum, and food suffer by comparison.
But, a few years hence, biology and space may be
supplanted by other research areas.

The stabilization of the rate of innovation in the
United States is also reflected in data published on the
activities of the U. S. Patent Office, presented in Table
2. The Patent Office in its present form was established
in 1836, although a patent organization has existed in
this country since 1790. [4] In seventeen years, 1836-53,
less than 1, 000 applications were filed each year. From
1853 to 1867, acceptances grew from under 1, 000 to
over 12, 000 a year. At this point, one might well have
expected that applications filed or accepted continued to
grow, year after year, and for many years this was
indeed the case. Since around 1920, however, the number
of patents have remained stable and even declined at
times--as in the 1940's, as a result of World War II.
The effect of the war shows up most strongly in the
1946-50 period, because the slow operation of the patent
office means that two or three years pass between the
filing of an application and the issuance of the patent for
an accepted application.

Generally speaking, by 1958 the rate of patent
activity had recovered from the effects of the war, as
can be seen in Table 2. But, we must not let the table
fool us into thinking that the number of patents issued
is once more increasing rapidly from year to year.
In 1964, although 93, 170 patents were applied for, only
47, 378 patents were issued (most of which were applied
for in 1962 and 1963). These figures are very comparable to the period 1931-35, when applications averaged
over 90, 000 a year, and patents granted yearly averaged
45, 640. In other words, the ratio of two applications

TABLE 2

AVERAGE ANNUAL NUMBER OF PATENTS
ISSUED TO INDIVIDUALS AND TO U. S. FIRMS
(Thousands)

Years	Individuals	Firms	Total	Percentage Distribution Individuals	Firms
1901 & 1906	22,823	5,205	28,028	81.4	18.6
1911 & 1916	28,249	9,560	37,809	74.7	25.3
1921-2-3-4-5	28,198	11,632	39,830	70.8	29.2
1926-7-8-9-30	25,300	17,260	42,560	59.4	40.6
1931-2-3-4-5	22,619	22,998	45,617	49.6	50.4
1936-7-8-9-40	17,030	20,928	37,958	44.9	55.1
1941-2-3-4-5	12,225	19,021	31,246	39.1	60.9
1946-7-8-9-50	11,791	15,675	27,466	42.9	57.1
1951-2-3-4-5	15,692	20,056	35,748	43.9	56.1
1956 & 1957	15,899	24,379	40,278	39.5	60.5

Source: U. S. Bureau of the Census, Historical Statistics of the United States (Washington, D. C.: U. S. Government Printing Office, 1960), p. 607.

for each patent issued seems to stand up over time. Patent
activities seem to have leveled off near the previous peak
around 1930.

An interesting question remains, why the number
of patents issued does not continue to grow, when actual
research and development expenditures increase, even
though expenditures have stabilized as a percentage of
Gross National Product. Basically, the answer may be
found in the fact that nowadays 60 per cent of patents
are issued to corporations, rather than individuals, whereas before 1900, less than 20 per cent were issued to corporations.

For a number of reasons, [5] in recent years
corporations have preferred not to file applications with
the Patent Office for the new processes and products.
First, when patent applications are filed, the information
on new products or processes becomes public knowledge,
and a rival business firm can easily and quickly adopt the
innovation, with perhaps minor changes to avoid infringe-
ment of patent rights. Thus, the advantage to the inventor
is lost almost as soon as it is gained. But, if no patent
application is filed, the details can be kept secret, and
it may be some time before a rival discovers them.

Another reason that patents have become less
valuable to corporations is that recent court and Department of Justice antitrust decisions have reflected a growing hostility to patents in general, and corporately held
patents in particular. Space does not permit us to discuss
this in detail, but between 1925 and 1929 in only 33 per
cent of the cases brought to court were patents judged
to be in violation of the antitrust laws, whereas between
1950 and 1954, this figure rose to 61 per cent, or almost
double.

Of course, the Antitrust Division of the Department of Justice brought under survey only a few hundred
outstanding patents from among the many tens of thousands issued. The interesting thing is that, although
the actual number of cases declined, the proportion of
those judged to be monopolistic increased.

Another factor discouraging corporate patenting may be seen in the following data: In 1953, companies with 5,000 or more employees spent more than $2,400 on research and development for each patent application they had pending, while companies with less than 5,000 employees spent only $1,100. While other factors enter into these differences, the greater vulnerability of large enterprises to compulsory licensing decrees in antitrust proceedings undoubtedly made a marked contribution.

The government has deterred the growth in the number of patents in other ways. From 1946 to 1957, the federal government performed between 16 and 26 per cent of all research and development work measured in dollar outlay, but it received less than 3 per cent of all patents issued. The reason for this is obvious--most government research is of a military character, and, as noted above, applying for patents would require public disclosure of details. Even the nonmilitary results of research are seldom patented, because they often depend upon or are related to results of military importance.

We can summarize this position as follows:

Since the government, from the outset of World War II has financed a large proportion of research and development, it must be assumed that much of the failure of corporate patenting to grow appreciably over the same period lies partly in the fact that many of the patents which would result would lack commercial value. The extent of government participation in financing R & D is indicated by the fact that in 1953, a year more or less typical of the period, thirty-seven percent of corporate R & D expenditures were financed by the federal government. [6]

In addition, there is the government's practice of requiring nonexclusive rights to inventions developed under government research or production contracts. With such rights, the government may permit another firm, doing work for the government, to use the invention.

Finally, the increasing delay in the handling of patent applications has also discouraged patenting. The budget of the Patent Office, and the number of patent officers required to consider and validate applications have not grown commensurately with either expanded research and development expenditures, nor even with inflation. During World War I, about one year usually elapsed between filing of an application and issuance of a patent; in the interwar period this lag increased to two years; and since the end of World War II, it has grown to about three years. The time lag now is often longer than the useful life of the patented item, particularly since other corporations may use the information to their own advantage as soon as the application is filed.

We have seen, in general, why the number of patents has not grown in recent years. Of course, no one can be certain whether the number will increase or decrease in the future. In the case of the government, expansion is not likely, because investigations and developments of nuclear power, perhaps its most patentable fundamental research work, are almost completed.

Corporate patent activity is another matter. That may increase, depending on the lag between patent application and patent issuance. If this period of time could be noticeably reduced, then, I am convinced, many inventions, which are now used in secret, would be patented and made public in the normal way. At present, however, the data on patents issued makes it clear that only a third or at most a half of the achievements of research and development expenditures (except those for military use) are publicly recorded through patenting procedures.

Another question is why, at present, inventive activities have more effect on the developed than the underdeveloped countries. One reason is that less-advanced countries are able to invest a relatively small share of their very limited resources in scientific progress. Let us consider a few of the more developed countries. During 1962, the United States had a total expenditure for research and development of $17.531

billion, of which approximately $9.5 billion was private
expenditure, some of which was almost certainly govern-
ment-subsidized. In other words, roughly $8 billion was
spent by the government directly on technical innovations in research and development. For five countries
of Western Europe, the 1962 expenditures for research
and development were: England $1.775 billion, France
$1.108 billion, West Germany $1.105 billion, Holland
$239 million, and Belgium $133 million, or a total of
$4.360 billion. These figures are for total research
and development, private as well as military and space;
they represent the following percentages of Gross National
Product at market price: United States 3.1, England 2.2,
France 1.5, West Germany 1.3, Holland 1.8, and Belgium 1.0. [7]

      The annual expenditure of the Soviet Union is un-
known, but it is assumed that it at least equals the
total spent by the Western European countries, and
possibly exceeds it by $500 million. The Soviet expen-
diture, therefore, is estimated to be approximately
$4.8 billion annually.

      The distinction between private and military or
space research and development is sometimes doubtful
but, in general, one can assume the following annual
military and space expenditures in recent years: United
States, $9 billion; Canada, $75 million; England, $690
million; France, $330 million; West Germany, $215 million; and Belgium, $6 million. [8] The percentages of
total research and development expenditures allotted to
private and nonmilitary purposes were: United States,
48; Canada, 87; England, 60; France, 75; West Germany,
80; and Belgium, 97. Thus, for example, of the $1.775
billion total spent by England in 1962 for both military
and nonmilitary research and development, $690 million
was spent for military and space; Belgium in 1964 spent
approximately $200 million for total research and develop-
ment, of which $6 million was for military and space. In
other words, in the European countries approximately
$1.25 billion was spent for military purposes and over $3
billion was spent for peaceful research.

If we examined all the countries of the non-Communist world, we would find that at least a third of research and development expenditures went for military purposes; in the United States about half was spent for war purposes, while the major European countries spent together about a third. Expenditures of the Soviet Union and China are not known, but it is safe to assume that the U. S. S. R. spends 50 or even 60 per cent on military research and development, although China probably spends a lot less. For the whole world, research and development expenditures, both military and nonmilitary, probably total $25 billion; however, the participation of less-developed nations is negligible.

Another explanation is the large immigration to developed countries, and particularly to the United States, of foreign engineers, scientists, and teachers. While precise data are not available, it is clear that of all countries, the United States is the primary destination for scientific emigrants. In the thirteen years from 1949 to 1960, 43, 500 scientists and engineers, or an average of 3, 350 per year, immigrated. The number was quite low in 1949, about 1,200; rose to 5, 800 in 1957; and declined to about 4, 000 in 1961. Graduates from foreign universities coming to the United States for their first jobs added about 3. 2 per cent to the output of scientists and engineers from American universities.[9] Some 2, 000 of the immigrants during this period could be considered refugees; of the others, 70 per cent came from European countries, 20 per cent from Latin America and Asia, and the remainder are unclassified as to the origin.

A majority of these immigrants came from countries with relatively high standards of living, underscoring the opinion that relative rather than absolute standards of living establish incentives for migration. Even so, the number of gifted men coming here from Europe is not sufficiently large to greatly deter European scientific progress. Immigration from Latin America and Asia, on the other hand, has caused a weakening in the scientific status of these areas and, in some cases, a decline in growth. These immigrants should not be compared with American scientists who travel for a year or more to underdeveloped countries, for their temporary absence from this country has little effect on the continued scientific development in the United States. [10]

Although the United States is especially attractive to scientists in other countries, because of the comparatively high incomes, job security, and research facilities, the more-developed countries of Europe were also attracting scientists and engineers from the less-advanced countries. Thus, we find many cases of Africans emigrating to France, and of scientists and engineers from India and other parts of Asia going to England and other European countries.

Finally, there is the problem of patent protection in underdeveloped countries. By and large, these countries have only a meager system for the protection of patent owners. Even when a new development occurs, only the wealthiest inventors can afford to patent it.

During the next thirty or forty years, the population of the whole world, and especially in underdeveloped countries, will undergo a rapid increase. But there is little likelihood of a commensurate growth in the number of scientific and technical personnel, and the pressure to keep scientific progress apace of the world's needs will constitute an ever-increasing burden on them.

Even with the expected growth in the number of colleges and universities, the majority of academic scientists will be obliged to continue to devote much of their efforts to teaching, with very little time left for research. The increased demands for education in all countries may leave even less time for research of a basic nature than is the case today.

The present-day gap between the developed and underdeveloped countries, which is especially great if measured by the standard of research and development efforts, will become even greater by the year 2000. Today, the over 2 billion inhabitants of the less-advanced countries are represented by a very small educated class. Because it is so small, the responsibilities of the organization and administration of governments weigh heavily upon its members, making it virtually impossible for those who could contribute to scientific and technical progress through research to do so.

In forty years, the only difference will be that this small group, even if it grows rapidly, will be responsible for 4 billion people instead of 2 billion. Therefore, I see little possibility for the countries which are underdeveloped today to catch up with the developed ones in the immediate future.

NOTES

1. C. F. Stover, The Government of Science (Santa Barbara, California: Center for the Study of Democratic Institutions, 1962), p. 3.

2. The discussion in the next two or three pages is from Kenneth E. Boulding, "The Wisdom of Man and the Wisdom of God" (1966). (Mimeographed.)

3. The figures are taken from Mohiuddin Ahmed, "World Population Growth and Levels of Living Trends, Patterns, Problems" (1965), p. 14. (Mimeographed.)

4. The Story of The United States Patent Office (Washington, D. C.: U. S. Government Printing Office, 1965), pp. 33-34.

5. Jacob Schmookler, "A Critique of Patent Statistics and a Review of the Literature"(circa 1958), pp. 13-24. (Mimeographed.)

6. National Science Foundation, Science and Engineering in American Industry, Final Report on a 1953-54 Survey (Washington, D. C.: U. S. Government Printing Office, 1956), p. 66.

7. E. M. Friedwald, "The Research Effort of Western Europe, the USA and the USSR," OECD Observer, Special Issue (February, 1966), pp. 10-15.

8. Organization for Economic Cooperation and Development, Government and Technical Innovation, Background Report for Second Ministerial Meeting on Science (Paris: OECD, January, 1966).

9. An estimate of foreign experts in the United States in the article by Mr. Friedwald, previously cited, shows annual average immigration of 4, 869 scientists and engineers to the United States for the years 1956-61. This figure is similar to the figure of annual average immigration of approximately 4, 000 foreign scientists to the United States for 1949-60.

10. Charles V. Kidd, "The Loss of Scientists from Less to More Developed Countries, " in U. S. Agency for International Development, Science, Technology, and Development, U. S. Papers Prepared for the U. N. Conference on the Application of Science and Technology for the Benefit of the Less Developed Areas, Vol. IX: Scientific and Technological Policy, Planning and Organization (Washington, D. C. : U. S. Government Printing Office, 1963), pp. 20-21.

COMMENTS BY SIMON TEITEL*

Although Professor Hoselitz presents several interesting points in his chapter, I think one could safely summarize its main thrust by means of the following propositions: (a) There is a slowdown in the rate of scientific advance; (b) scientific advances originating in the rich countries will be of insignificant benefit to the less-developed countries.

Professor Hoselitz tries to show, first, that the rate of scientific advance is not greater today than it was in the late nineteenth and early twentieth centuries. He uses the proportion of Gross National Product going into research and development and the number of patents granted in the United States as a measure of scientific advance. These are rather poor indicators of the rate of technological or scientific progress, and Hoselitz discusses some of their shortcomings. But, even less warranted is the jump from (a) to (b), namely, the conclusion that scientific advances will be of very small benefit to the less-developed countries. Such a conclusion appears especially shaky if one takes into account the enormous gulf that lies between the stock of available knowledge in the advanced countries and the level of technology used by the less-developed countries. Hoselitz' argument consists of showing, with projected rates of world population growth and changes in its distribution, that the poor will continue to be relatively poor. While it may be accepted that the less-developed areas will not achieve, in the near future, the rate of innovation of the United States, it is still foreseeable that the application of some scientific and technological advances may have a very strong impact in the developing world. Examples which come immediately to one's mind are: fertilizers, new birth control methods, nuclear power, water desalinization, weather prediction and control, satellite

---

*Dr. S. Teitel is associated with the United Nations. Opinions here expressed are those of the author and do not necessarily represent the point of view of the United Nations.

communications, use of plastics in housing construction, many computer applications, and so forth.

Professor Hoselitz claims that the United States has already reached diminishing returns with "labor-widening" type of expansion in research and development expenditures, and also that demand for the research personnel exceeded supply during the period ranging from the 1920's to the 1950's. First, with reference to the demand-supply imbalance, Professor Hoselitz offers as evidence the advertisements for engineering and scientific personnel in the Sunday edition of The Chicago Tribune. It is my impression that these are, to a large extent, image-building type of ads, less concerned with filling any particular post than with advertising the scientific research-mindedness and progressiveness of a given company. This is probably more common in the case of large firms. Such a device provides also the opportunity of building up in advance, at low cost, sources of supply of technical and scientific personnel.

Furthermore, I do not know what exact meaning Professor Hoselitz ascribes to his statement. Is it that wages for research type of personnel have been too low for the equilibrium in a competitive market, and that consequently they are rising rapidly? One could perhaps argue that the scarcity of research labor is due to the large divergences between returns to the individual and to the society resulting from institutional constraints.

Hoselitz' argument about decreasing returns can be restated in terms of relative growth rates. If the growth of factors other than labor used in research has been much more rapid than that of labor, the latter could be considered relatively fixed, and, from that point of view, one could talk about decreasing returns to the other variable factors, not to the labor.

At the beginning of his study, Hoselitz comments about a take-off in rational science and

asks: Why it did not happen long ago in China? With
adequate modifications, this may be the relevant question to ask about less-developed countries today.
Perhaps the strategic variable is not the rationality
about or in the scientific field, but lies in the application of the results of scientific discoveries and technological innovations to practical purposes like the production of goods and services. [1]

The important point, according to Professor
Hoselitz, is when the scientific revolution starts to
affect the economic and social life of the mass of the
population, i. e. , when major industries begin to become dependent on technical knowledge. Hoselitz
raises here a problem important for the countries in
the process of development. He notes that it is
impossible to estimate the scientific base of industry
in advanced countries; the implication apparently
being that most of their modern industries could not
have been established without pre-existing scientific
inventions and development.

In this respect, it seems very important to
find a methodology for measuring and expressing the
dependency of modern industry on science and technology. The difference between the two worlds, of
which Hoselitz speaks, lies in the extent to which new
products, modern production methods, equipment,
and control practices are incorporated into industrial
production.

Professor Hoselitz also mentions the brain-
drain from the developing countries. Some scholars
argue that the brain-drain is due to the absence of
autonomous innovations or sources of technological
progress in the less-developed countries. According
to Hoselitz, the explanation of a very slow growth in
these countries is that professionals and scientists
have no choice but to resort to other activities, or
to emigrate. Some empirical evidence exists on
this subject, and analysis of the data of Argentina,
for example, suggests that, in recent years, emigra-
tion of scientists, engineers, and other professionals

(such as physicians and teachers) has been closely correlated with the level of economic activity and the rate
of economic growth. It does not seem to work the other
way around. It is precisely because of the lack of opportunities in their own countries that these people emigrate.

My final comment is on the problem of the
transfer of technology. Broadly speaking, the less-
developed countries copy or adapt the technology from
developed countries. The question is: What type of
technology to choose? Three different schools of
thought seem to prevail:

(1) The "revivalists" suggest that the less-
developed countries should apply old technologies considered obsolete and discarded by the industrial countries. Examples of this view would be such programs
as the Chinese big "leap forward, " or iron furnaces in
the backyard, Ghandi's return to the spinning wheel
and handloom, and so forth.

(2) Proponents of "intermediate" technologies
argue that less-developed countries should use techniques appropriate to their factor endowments, techniques which do not exist because industrial technology
in the developed countries has been designed for the
factor proportions and factor prices prevailing there.

(3) The "modernists" advocate the application,
as soon as possible and on as large scale as feasible,
of the most modern and advanced techniques.

Supporters of points of view (1) and (2) generally
favor small-scale industries, secondhand machinery,
and labor-intensive industries and techniques. Without
discussing the theoretical argument, the empirical
evidence supports the view that modern manufacturing
processes offer little choice between alternative techniques, which are similarly efficient, but differ to a
significant degree in their factor intensity. In practice,
the choice between more or less labor-intensive techniques usually reduces to a choice between products.[2]
The modern techniques transferred to the less-developed

countries are typically characterized by large scale of production, high skills, and capital requirements.

Some consequences of the transfer of these technologies may be sketched in brief:

(1) Economic scale of production must be large in relation to the market size of most countries, even after allowance is made for some scaling down. Size is also necessary to reap comparative advantage in export industries that are based on local resources.

(2) Consequently, the structure of industry in the less-developed countries will tend to be monopolistic. There is a case, then, for government regulation or ownership. Control is made more difficult whenever local government is dealing with branches of foreign companies.

(3) Sometimes, allegedly to counteract this difficulty and to preserve competition, two or more inefficient producers are encouraged, with waste and oligopoly as a result.

(4) Because of the above-mentioned limitation of market size, a case can be made for the promotion of industrial exports, in order to provide an additional outlet, until domestic demand catches up with the economic scale of output.

Even these points may be self-deluding, because, in the past, economists had actually very little to say about the transfer of technology. After all, in economic theory, technology, like tastes, has been assumed to be exogenous and given.

NOTES TO COMMENTS

1. A comparison between Europe and the United States in a field such as chemistry, for example, illustrates this point. The attention paid in the United States to chemical engineering, as opposed to the concentration on basic chemistry in Europe, is probably one of the explanations for the relative technological leadership maintained in this field by the American industry, despite the fact that the basic work of chemical synthesis was done in many cases in European laboratories.

2. United Nations, World Economic Survey 1964, Part I, Development Plans: Appraisal of Targets and Progress in Developing Countries (United Nations Publication, Sales No. 65. II. C. 1), p. 66.

COMMENTS BY RICHARD R. NELSON

There are two factual assertions in Professor Hoselitz' intended message. The first is that the rate of advance in scientific and technical knowledge is leveling off in developed countries. The second is that future advances in science and technology will primarily benefit the countries that already are rich, and be of very limited benefit to the backward countries. Although the pattern of evidence presented by Professor Hoselitz does not provide sufficient support for his double-barreled assertion, I intend first to show that Professor Hoselitz' contentions may not be very important to the less-developed countries. Second, a few remarks will be added on the usefulness of the concept of technological transfer.

Let us assume that in the future no new technology relevant to the less-developed countries were to be developed in the advanced countries. If there were opportunities to update and improve the technologies in use in underdeveloped countries to a point close to that which the advanced economies already have achieved, this alone would permit a tremendous increment to standards of living in less-developed countries. Certainly, the question of technology transfer is interesting even if there will not be any relevant new technology developed in the advanced countries.

But to what extent is the concept of technological transfer a useful one? To what extent is it useful to state that breakdown of the technology transfer mechanism is a major cause of the great discrepancies that exist at the present time between incomes in the poor countries and incomes in the United States? To what extent can policy be usefully guided by a goal of improving the technology transfer mechanism? While I consider that transfer of technology is a useful concept, a case may be argued that it is not.

In a country like Colombia, productivity per worker in industry averages one-fourth of that in the United States, depending on the industry, and the technology in use certainly is different from ours. But it is far from

sufficient to argue that the lack of technological transfer
is preventing progress in Colombia.   There are other,
rather straightforward explanations of the difference in
economic growth, for example, the framework of neoclassical theory.   Businessmen in all countries face
roughly the same spectrum of technological options.
Given the factor supplies which exist in less-developed
countries, businessmen and managers select technologies they find to be the cheapest or the most profitable.   In the less-developed countries, unskilled labor
is extremely plentiful and cheap; physical capital is
scarce and expensive, and so is skilled and highly
educated labor.   Therefore, less-developed countries
choose technologies that use a very high proportion of
unskilled labor, and that economize on skills and
physical capital.   Thus, this explanation within the
framework of the straightforward neoclassical production function can account for differences in levels of
output per worker.

        According to this view, the problems of less-
developed countries are simply the result of shortages
of different types of factors, skills, and capital; and there
is no need to invoke a concept like technological transfer.
Any policies to assist the less-developed countries
should aim to augment the supply of skills and capital,
which, in itself, will naturally lead to a change in the
technology used.   An attempt to effect technical change
without factor augmentation would be futile or pernicious.
Given factor supplies, technologies in use are pretty
much the optimal technologies.

        However, contrary to the neoclassical theory, I
maintain that differences among   factor supplies,
environment, remuneration, productivity, capital stock,
etc., do not explain the gap in incomes and economic
development attained by various countries.   After all
these factors are accounted for, a large residual
remains, and one way to explain the residual difference
is that technology in the less-developed countries is
inferior, and has a lower productivity per unit of labor,
compared to that of the United States or the United
Kingdom.   Therefore, it is convenient to phrase the

difference as a technological gap.   It is a useful concept
primarily for operational types of work such as research
by Spencer on the process by which aircraft manufacturing
technology in the United States was introduced in the
aircraft manufacturing industry in Japan. [1] As a result,
Japanese productivity in aircraft manufacturing increased
immensely.   It is exactly the kind of study which, with
other similar ones, I consider meaningful, and I find
that the mechanism of technological transfer is an interesting and worthwhile concept for further exploration.
In this operational context, lies the validity and vitality
of transfer of technology.

NOTE TO COMMENTS

1. Daniel L. Spencer, "An External Military
Presence, Technological Transfer, and Structural
Change," Kyklos, XVIII (1965), 451-74.

CHAPTER 5 TRANSFER OF TECHNOLOGY AND SIMULATION STUDIES

by Martin Shubik

INTRODUCTION

The two major themes developed in this chapter are that simulation studies provide a useful new way of investigating the transfer and diffusion of technology, and that the studies, in and of themselves, may play a role in the diffusion of economic and social change.

Both mathematical models and simulations of an economy may be viewed as alternative forms of economic history.[1] The difference between the usual form of economic history and a mathematical model is that the latter tends to be more precise, more restricted, poorer in description but better in logical structure and in depth of analysis (in a rather restricted sense). A simulation lies in between a mathematical model and a verbal description. It is broader and more flexible than the former and more precise and structured than the latter. The second theme is that simulation studies are naturally suited to aid in the development of planning institutions. These institutions may serve as the means to accelerate the transfer of new technology by increasing the diffusion of knowledge and preparing the social climate for the acceptance of the new and foreign.

SIMULATION

In the past few years, the word "simulation" has begun to make its way into economic literature.[2] The word is old, especially in reference to other areas in which analogue simulation has been used for some time. For example, the air frame industry has utilized

physical models in wind tunnel simulations; for teaching
purposes, a   hydraulic model at the London School of
Economics has provided an analogue simulation of a
macroeconomic system for many years.   This particular
model has been excellently illustrated by the English
cartoonist Emett in Punch of 1953.

A simulation of a system or an organism is the
operation of a model or simulator, which is a representation of the system or organism.   The model is amenable
to manipulations that would be impossible, too expensive,
or impracticable to perform on the entity it portrays.
The operation of the model can be studied, and from it
properties concerning the behavior of the actual system
or its subsystems can be inferred.

Mathematical Models and Simulations

Simulations are closely related to the mathematical models.   Two types of mathematical models are
familiar to most economists interested in growth and
international trade.   They are sequential models with
relations formulated in terms of difference or differential equations; and models involving the simultaneous
evaluation of several variables given a set of relationships between the variables.

A simple example of the first type might consist
of three or four highly aggregate accounting and behavioral
equations in which, as in the example below, the whole
economy is represented by two or three sectors, and each
sector is represented by a single behavioral relation meant
to typify all actions of that sector.

$$Y_t = G_t + I_t + C_t \qquad \text{(Accounting relation)}$$

$$C_t = \alpha Y_{t-1} \qquad \text{(Behavior relation)}$$

$$I_t = \beta(C_t - C_{t-1}) \qquad \text{(Behavior relation)}$$

$$G_t = k \qquad \text{(Behavior relation} \\ \text{--Policy Control--)}$$

where Y_t = Gross National Product in time   t

G_t = Government spending in time   t

C_t = Consumption in time   t

I_t = Private investment in time   t

Given, that care has been taken to specify the ranges of definition of these relationships, in a case as simple as the one given here, we could solve the system mathematically with little difficulty, and (if we believed that it were a reasonably good representation of reality) we could directly examine the effect of changes in the parameters.

In this model, a limited amount of the exploration of government policy can be made by observing the effect of different size k's. Suppose, however, we wished to consider a countercyclical policy related to the level of unemployment and to the growth rate of Gross National Product. It would be necessary to replace the expression for G_t by a far more complex relation or set of relations, such as:

$$G_t = k_1 \ [u_{t-1}]_\rho \ + k_2 \ [Y_{t-1} - Y_{t-2}] \ .$$

Even a relatively simple modification, such as that represented by this policy, makes a mathematical treatment essentially unmanageable. The mathematical difficulties will depend upon the exponent ρ and furthermore an extra relation, or set of relations, will be needed to update the values of u_t, the level of unemployment at time t. However, the simulation of the time series generated by the new system is no more difficult than the simulation of the time series generated by the first system.

In the first example, the set of equations, the mathematical expressions for Y_t, C_t and I_t as functions of time and the parameters, and the time series produced by a simulation can all be regarded as solutions to the problem of predicting future states of the system. However, these three different solution concepts are of varying usefulness to the individual who wants to

answer specific questions.   The first solution is of use
only to the person of sufficient genius, who can immediately deduce the implications contained in a consistent
and complete set of relations without having to "solve"
them further.   When an explicit expression exists for
the variables of interest, it usually will be a more useful solution than the time series, because it is more
compact and may be mathematically manipulated directly
to answer questions concerning the sensitivity of parameters.   For example if our solution shows that:

$$Y_t = A_1 \, \alpha [\, (1-\beta) \, + \, \sqrt{1-4\beta^2}] \, ^t + A_2 \, \alpha [(1-\beta) - \sqrt{1-4\beta^2} \,] \, t$$

we can immediately examine the derivatives $\partial Y_t / \partial_1 \alpha$ and
$\partial Y_t / \partial_1 \beta$ to estimate the behavior of Y_t as α and β vary.
The same sensitivity search could be made by simulating
with the original equation system and feeding in a series
of different values for α and β, then comparing the
resultant time series.   For the modified set of equations,
it is quite likely that an explicit compact specification
of the relevant variables in terms of time and the parameters does not exist.   In this case, the time series
obtained from simulation may be our only source of insight into the dynamics of the model.

In general, the sensitivity testing of large dynamic
systems is difficult and expensive.   It is still probably
more of a scientific art than a formalized procedure.
The mere fact that the techniques of simulation permit
the easy generation of time series does not mean that
easy exhaustive procedures exist for the exploration of
the sensitivity of complex models.   The combinatorics
of different values for different parameters mitigates
against this.   The success of the search by simulation
rests heavily upon the substantive knowledge of the
problem and a sufficient understanding, to be able to
interpret the findings.   It is a form of economic history,
and, as such, all the art and talent of an historian are
still necessary in order to select the relevant path
through the morass of alternatives.

The second type of mathematical model familiar to economists is one that involves simultaneous relationships, the simplest example being linear supply and demand conditions. Suppose we have supply and demand given by $s_t = a + bp_t$ and $g_t = c + dp_t$. If we assume that there is a market mechanism, which brings about a price that equates supply and demand, then we can find the p_t^* and the $s_t^* = q_t^*$ by solving the three equations.

A simulation performs its steps in tracing out a time path by operating on all relations sequentially. Hence, in general it does not cope with the simultaneous relations. However, it is both easy and sometimes necessary to include simultaneous relations in a simulation to solve that part by analytic or iterative procedures, and then proceed sequentially through the rest of the program.

There are various reasons for including simultaneous relations in a simulation. It has been argued that in economic life simultaneity is not really needed, because by the use of a sufficiently small quantum of time the error, introduced by assuming the existence of a lag, will be so small that it can be safely ignored. Thus, if the $\Delta t = t - (t-1)$ is small enough,

$$s_t = a + bp_t \qquad\qquad s_t = a + bp_{t-1}$$
$$\text{or}$$
$$q_t = c + dp_t \qquad\qquad q_t = c + dp_{t-1}$$

will give approximately the same results. This is certainly not mathematically sound in any very general way, but for many situations of economic interest may be sufficiently true. It is almost always bound to be false, however, if the time increment is large. The natural time units for the socio-economic simulations of any size are a week, month, quarter, or year. In general, it is very difficult to obtain large masses of data on a weekly or monthly basis, and furthermore, even though computers are fast, there is around a fifty-to-one running time difference between a weekly or annual time basis. If, owing to considerations of the availability and quality of data, simulation time, or output processing, a quarterly or yearly time scale

is used, then the errors introduced by replacing an
equation such as $C_t = \alpha Y_t$ by $C_t = \alpha Y_{t-1}$ are large.
In order to avoid such errors and still use a large
time scale it is necessary to include simultaneous
relations and solve them.

Leaving the technical details of data gathering
and computation aside, we are often confronted in our
description of a process with the problems of interaction between different factors. Does social change
set up the preconditions for technological change or
vice versa? Often, the answer is that both influence
each other simultaneously. This possibility may be
studied by using a mathematical model containing
equation systems calling for simultaneous solution.

Behavior Equations or Explicit Maximization

An important distinction between different models
of behavior is whether they are presented as the result
of some more basic optimizing process explicitly, or
merely as behavior that may or may not have implicitly
an explanation based on optimization. For example, we
may describe the behavior of a consumer by first stating
that we have (say by psychometric experimentation)
determined his preference system, which is given by
$U = -a(M-x)^2 + y$ where x and y are quantities of two
goods; then observing that if the exchange rate between
the two is such that $y = px$, he acts to:

$$\text{Maximize}_{x} \ \ U = -a(M-x)^2 + px.$$

We might also have a behavior equation which states that
x is chosen to satisfy:

$$x = M - \frac{p}{2a}.$$

We could say that the latter equation implicitly represents
the maximization process of the consumer described by
the former equation. The former implies the latter but
not vice versa. Generally, a simulation will contain
behavior relations and not explicit optimization processes.
It is a matter of economic, political, or other observations,

theories, and measurements to decide whether the
behavior equations are implied by specific optimization
processes.

The policy-maker or experimenter interested
in control and in some criterion of optimality may
easily want to use a simulation to explore the implications of various policies. If he is interested in optimization, he can explore for an optimal policy implicitly
by varying parameters or changing the structure of the
policy equations, observing the different time series
generated, and comparing their optimality according
to some objective function or criterion outside of the
simulation. For example, in the equations in the preceding section, government policy was given by:

$$G_t = k.$$

We could try various values of k and obtain time series
for them. Our objective function might be a function of
the size of the fluctuations in the business cycle. It
would then be possible to judge the worth of the different
k, or of alternative policies calling for more complex
government behavior.

It is, of course, possible to include an explicit
maximization process in part of the program of a simulation; however, the methods of simulation are used
generally in situations in which the explicit maximization
problem cannot necessarily be set up, and even if it
can be, then it is beyond mathematical analysis. An
important example of the relationship between program-
ming and algorithm methods and simulation is provided
by the various large process models of the operation
of oil refineries. The objective function is usually more
or less well-defined, and the processes can be described
with a high degree of accuracy. Unless there are highly
complex, nonlinear interrelations, the whole process
can be described in terms of a large linear or quadratic
program, which may be solved by the appropriate
algorithms to yield directly an optimum policy. Beyond
some level of complexity, however, a simulation of the
process may be as much as can be done.

In one sense, the exclusion of the objective
function as an explicit part of a simulation is desirable.
It means, in particular, that there is a more or less
natural separation of the policy considerations and of
the problem of describing the socio-economic environment. This can be useful in focusing on the problems
of communication between policy-oriented individuals
and behavioral scientists. Furthermore, in many
attempts to study learning processes, cultural change,
and the spread of ideas, explicit maximization or optimization processes may not provide the best description.

Simulation and Gaming

This section is included merely to clear up some
misconceptions that have arisen concerning the use of
three different approaches to social, political, and
economic problems. We are using the word "simulation"
to refer to the computer "operation" of a (sociopolitico-
economic) model. The rules of operation are specified
by the behavioral and accounting equations. Uncertainty
in measurement or other forms of uncertainty may be
accounted for by the presence of random variables in
the model. However, once the model has been formalized, the insights and errors of its builder will be
reflected without question by the simulation. The word
"simulation" has also been used in a somewhat different
meaning[3] to refer to situations in which people play
the roles of decision-makers in more or less formally
simulated environments. This type of investigation is
also referred to as "gaming. " The key difference
between what we wish to refer to as simulation and
as gaming is that the former involves the manipulation
of a mathematical model with no direct participation
of individuals, whereas the latter always involves the
active participation of people as an integral part of
the exercise. Simulation and gaming may easily be
used as complementary investigations. For example,
in situations where alternative policies are being
explored one can use a simulation of the variety described above to serve as the basis for a gaming
exercise, in which instead of having explicit formulae
for, e. g. , government policy and foreign trade policy,

two sets of players make each period their decisions
based upon the information supplied by the other parts
of the model.

Gaming, especially with players simulating the
roles of decision-makers, has been used for teaching,
training, operational, and experimental purposes. [4]
Our immediate concern is with simulation, hence further
discussion of gaming is postponed until the section
"Institutions, Technological Change, and Simulation."

Game theory is a third topic often confused with
simulation and gaming. It is often relevant to gaming
exercises or to the construction of simulations, but it
is by no means the same as either. The theory of games
is basically a mathematical theory devoted to the study
of problems of strategy, conflict, and cooperation. It
is implicitly relevant to the type of simulation described
here, inasmuch as the social, political, or economic
forces may reflect situations that cannot be described
even explicitly in terms of maximization, but must be
thought of in terms of varying levels of conflict and
cooperation. [5] However, it must be stressed that the
relevance of game theory is at the conceptual level,
inasmuch as the conflict and cooperation in the society
will have already been reflected in the behavior equations.

Growth, Diffusion, and Social Process

The lessons of history, sociology, and psychology
have been at least partly learned by the economist, tech-
nologist, and physical scientist dealing with the relationship between the knowledge and techniques on the one side
and the individuals or society on the other. Production
engineering has shown an understanding of the importance
of "learning curves" in the setting up of new processes or
the introduction of new machines. In marketing, studies
have begun to appear concentrating on information processes within a society. The paths through which information
spreads, and the factors entering into the shaping of
opinion, are being investigated. The model of a man as
an information processor, and of the society as a communication network, is a far cry from the standard

economic models. This does not mean that such a
model is at odds with the theories of economic maximization; it simply means that there are important
aspects of socio-economic and politico-economic life
that are not adequately modelled by the rationalistic,
high information type of model of man which underlies
much of economic theory.

In take-off and growth situations, the role of
information processes becomes crucial, and the high
levels of information are required. In the strictly
technical study of information theory, the point has
been made that the volume of information is a function
of the change of states, and not necessarily of the
complexity of the original situation. The analogy with
human affairs is direct. A stable unchanging society
may have elaborate rituals and complex technology,
yet, except for the need to teach individuals their
roles, as they pass through the life cycle, the system
contains little information. There is little need for
flexibility, and although procedures may appear to
be intricate to the outsider, they are simple to the
initiated, inasmuch as they are unchanged over long
periods of time.

In the context of stability, it is not unreason-
able to assume that individuals become more or less
completely informed about the environment relevant
to their activity, and that their behavior (within their
circumscribed set of choices) can be explained by an
economic theory of choice. The introduction of new
technology is a challenge to stability. To facilitate
the absorption, the institutions and the social structure must be capable of absorbing the potential
disruption to communication and data processing
patterns. New technology includes not only new
physical objects but also new methods of using old
objects. Perhaps a better phrase than the introduction of new technology would be the ability to successfully implement a change in the process.

Various societies differ considerably in the
existence of institutions to routinize change. In many

sectors of the American industry a distinction is made between new product engineering, which modifies and varies existing products in a regular manner, and advanced research and development aimed at nonscheduled change. The difference appears to be primarily in the amount of uncertainty involved. It appears, however, that beyond some (ill-defined) range, a quantitative change in the level of uncertainty implies a qualitative change in the attitude of those concerned; at some level of uncertainty, development becomes research.

It is beyond the scope of this chapter to investigate the social, psychological, and political causes that lie behind the variety of conditions determining the great difference in diffusion rates in different countries and at different times. An analysis of the problems in the transfer of technology represents itself an attempt to influence the rates. The sociology of science does not appear to indicate that the society of scientists is necessarily more open to the inroads of the new and foreign any more than is a society of highland Indians.

However, the technology of the computer is available for transfer to the clans and societies of academe. Many inhabitants of academe may regard the intrusion of alien technology as undesirable. If they are strong and wrong, it may take a generation to wait for them to die (or even longer, if they are able to indoctrinate a priesthood). If they are strong and right, they will be able to repel "the strangers who came to try to teach them their ways. " The perceptions of the bearer of technological gifts are not always in harmony with the perceptions of the recipient.

As a proponent of the use of the computer in the behavioral sciences, it is my thesis that simulation may be used to investigate many worthwhile conjectures, hypotheses, and even theories concerning the diffusion of knowledge within a society and the conditions for the acceptance of change. Most of the investigation to date has been in verbal terms backed up with a few statistics. There is a broad group of

mathematical models, which have already been applied
to learning problems, to diffusion processes, and to
the analysis of growth, that appear to be directly
relevant to the study of the transfer of technology.
There are few behavioral scientists who are highly
skilled enough in mathematical techniques to be in
a position to manipulate more than some of the
simplest of the models. Even those who are in such
a position find that mathematical formulations of
sufficient richness and complexity may soon exceed
the possibilities of analysis.

Simulation provides a method for producing
time series of the behavior of systems far beyond
the scope of words and far beyond the limitations of
mathematical analysis. It offers the opportunity for
a blend of institutional and mathematical work. The
conjectures and insights of the historian of social
process can be enriched by a new, relatively fast,
and cheap analytical exploration device.

INSTITUTIONAL STUDIES, INSTITUTIONS, QUALITATIVE METHODS, AND PLANNING

The invention of new techniques and the devising
of plans are not enough to change the direction of societies. Planning institutions are needed; the process of
implementation and the distribution systems of knowledge
in a society may be as necessary for eventual success
as the existence of the knowledge itself. Two simple
and important examples in economics are provided by
the national income accounting schemes, which have
come into being since Keynes, and the input-output
tabulations based on the original work of Wassily
Leontief. Both of these have been of considerable
value to the growth and welfare of almost every
economy in the world. The major manifestation
of this value is in the institutions that have grown up
to regularize and transmit the gathering of information
in a framework accepted by those in power and used in
their decision processes.

The second major theme suggested here is
that simulation techniques aid in the creation of conditions for interdisciplinary work and in the construction
or improvement of planning institutions. Several general observations on this topic will be made and related
to the problem of technological transfer.

Institutional Studies and Models
as an Organizing Device

The joining together of results and insights
obtained from qualitative studies and quantitative studies
would be an important step in recreating a political or
social economy. In most instances, massive empirical
work, observation, discussion, and writing are needed
before concepts can be clarified, variables separated,
and formal model-building, quantification, and measurement can take place.

Good comprehensive descriptive studies are
always valuable; but, by themselves, they are often not
sufficient for a balanced understanding of a socio-
economy. Ordinary language provides for much
flexibility and a desirable lack of precision, which
prevents concepts from being overly formalized at
too early a stage; however, the price paid for this
lack of precision can be high. In particular (as has
already been noted with reference to large data
gathering systems) lengthy verbal descriptions of
complex multivariate systems may easily be inconsist-
ent or incomplete. The tendency for the argument to
lose coherence among different chapters of a book is
large. If such a book is presented as an overview of
social change, or if it presents a thesis or a theory
concerning development, it should be possible to
develop a simulation which at least reflects the
major ideas and serves as an organizing and consistency checking device for the study. It must be
stressed that this includes the possibility of representing many qualitative as well as quantitative
effects in the simulation.

The discipline of constructing a simulation
to reflect the major aspects of the observations and

the theory behind an institutional study can serve a far
more general and important role than providing organization and a consistency check. If there is an interest
in comparative study, by designing a common output,
the joint analysis of different cases is facilitated considerably.

Qualitative Methods and Measurement

Even now, there still probably exists a mis-
understanding between mathematically and nonmathe-
matically oriented behavioral scientists. It is often
assumed that there is a cleavage that separates those
interested in mathematical methods into a category
willing to ignore any phenomenon to which a number
cannot be attached. For many years, however, (at
least since Edgeworth and Pareto) there has been a
considerable development in methods for the study
of phenomena that cannot be measured by a single
number, or that need not be quantified at all. In-
difference curve analysis provides one such example.
More-advanced methods have been concerned with
the relative merits and uses of linear measures,
complete orderings, partial orderings, multidimen-
sional measures, lexicographic orderings, and so
forth. There are many phenomena involving political,
social, or economic choice for which the only information needed is that one choice is larger, preferred to,
less dangerous, or more sensible than the other.
By using the logical capabilities of a computer it is
possible to study processes based on this type of
consideration.

The Updated Book and Comparative Library

The communication revolution brought about by
the high-speed digital computer is certainly at least of
the same order of magnitude as the invention of the
printing press. The concepts of both book and library
will have to be and are being revised.

Books on applied social and economic topics,
such as country development studies, form, at this
time, a relatively hard to manipulate and hard to

update data bank.   When new information becomes available, it may be highly desirable to examine it in the context of the previous study, and possibly to revise a book.   The costs in both time and money make book revisions inordinately expensive.   If, however, a book has with it an associated simulation, which, in turn, is connected with a data processing scheme and an ongoing organization in the process of creating a data bank, the possibilities for revision are considerably improved.

Specifically, we consider three types of situations.   The first is the standard type of updating and experimentation that both the reader and writer would like to do if the time costs were relatively low.   They are able to update certain statistical information, and to ask a number of "what if" questions based on modifications to the hypotheses presented or on additional hypotheses.   A simulator written in relation to a book is an organized précis.   Clearly, it will not contain the richness of description and many of the finer shades of meaning that are contained in the book; however, if, for instance, there is a description of investment behavior, the simulation would reflect the main features of this behavior.   Consequently, alternative hypotheses in the context of the over-all work can be examined by changing the instructions representing investment.   In many works, painstaking original data gathering is necessary, and often the statistical tables presented come from nonroutine processing.   Once data have been gathered, if they are important, it may be possible to routinize their updating; if it is not, then obviously no simulation or formalized data handling system can help.   However, there is invariably a large amount of relevant data for which routinized processes can or do exist.   These serve as an updating input for the simulation which, in turn, means that many aspects of a book remain current, enlarging the basis for further work.

The second situation concerns joint work between academic research and planning groups, and quantitatively and qualitatively oriented individuals. In the preceding section, the relation between qualitative and quantitative methods has been discussed.

There is little question that a simulation is no substitute
for substantive knowledge and insight; it can, however,
be an organizing device for the substantive knowledge
and insights of many independent people. An interchange
is needed between governmental planning groups, other
agencies, and researchers in academic institutions. It
is needed because the former are in possession and
control of information that the latter need. The latter
are able to take a longer-term and more dispassionate
view of processes. Also the latter can provide insights
and a theoretical framework that helps to blend the long-
term with the short-term operational view.

        Once a model has been constructed, it serves as
a focal point for interchange. The over-all operation of
the model, with guesses and approximations, can be of
operational use, while the careful measurement of technological and behavioral relations and the redesign of
subroutines will, for the most part, be of direct academic
interest. Furthermore, both academics and others need
to improve methods and institutions for the more effective
interchange and use of information. There are large
increasing returns to scale in information handling, and
in joint model-building, which have not yet been realized.

        The third situation concerns the use of simulation
and formal models for comparative purposes and "library
cross-reference" for institutions or agencies engaged in
comparative studies. If an institution, such as the
International Monetary Fund or a university or government agency, has sponsored comparative studies, simulations related to each study may be used in the same format
for purposes of comparison. It is for this reason that,
in the model presented later in the chapter, the output
utilizes heavily the income accounts scheme of the Agency
for International Development. [6]

Institutions, Technological Change, and Simulation

        It is a premise of this chapter that, at least some of
us believe, the introduction of change of process in some
aspects of the socio-economy of many countries would be
desirable. There is a world-wide concern for growth,
development, and welfare. Given, however, that we are

unwilling, as a matter of principle, or unable to change
institutions in a radical manner, it becomes necessary
to seek evolutionary means to modify or create the
appropriate institutions. For success, in countries
such as those of Latin America, it is necessary to
establish a community of interest between the administrative hierarchy, the intellectuals, and the foreign
agencies that are concerned. Current experience
with simulation offers a very natural means for improving communications between administrators, politicians,
and scholars.

In my opinion, possibly the greatest drawback
of simulation is its fundamental attractiveness to
administrators and politicians, who want a "scientific
black box" to help them with their planning. The idea
of being able to construct dynamic models of an economy,
with which one can experiment on policy change, appeals
to the imagination. Yet, a new technology or methodology without substantive content may easily yield very
little. The mere presence of a new means of communication does not of itself guarantee that there will be anything worthwhile to communicate. However, without
the added possibility, communication of value may be
impeded.

Both at the level of the country and the corporation
there has been an increasing recognition of the value of
an integrated communication, information processing,
and decision system. Such a system calls for a basic
understanding of the meaning of information in the context of human organizations. Among other features,
this means an appreciation by all that valuable information to the scholar may be regarded as useless to the
administrator and meaningless to the public, mutatis
mutandis. The same raw data call for many different
aggregations to be of use to more than one decision
maker or investigator. A well-designed simulation
may be regarded as an aggregating, disaggregating
device that can utilize the same bank of raw data to
produce different displays of value to individuals
with divergent interests.

The importance of better communication between diverse groups is, in my estimation, greater in countries lacking institutions designed to routinize economic change, than in countries, such as the United States, where many economic problems can be looked at primarily as economic problems alone. Even in the United States, many of the greatest problems, such as the growth of the cities, pollution, inter-urban transportation, and so forth, involve a blend of economics, sociology, and politics. In most countries of the world with low per capita incomes this holds true of almost every so-called economic problem. Thus, literacy, agrarian reform, tax collection, nutrition, or slum clearance—each are problems with an economic aspect; but mere aid and money may easily do nothing whatsoever to solve them.

In these countries technological change is very much related to social process. It is for this reason that, in spite of their undoubted use, input-output matrices of underdeveloped areas may be of far less value than their proponents may believe. This is especially true when international comparisons are made. Input-output tables are a form of a production function, and reflect in a gross way technological relationships with the social structure implicit in the relationships. Production functions are, in general, a poor representation of institutions of production. If we are interested in a static situation, they may be sufficient for many economic purposes. This is especially true in countries such as the U. S. or U. S. S. R. ; however, in underdeveloped areas even minor economic change is difficult without social change. When we wish to consider serious technological change, a static input-output table may aid in building up a false sense of security and a false impression of our technical knowledge of the country's socio-economic means of producing wealth. Sociological variables, diffusion processes, and representations of social and socio-political change must be blended with economic information and plans for the successful implementation of technological change. Means for coordinating the joint work necessary for this blending are of paramount importance. A simulation can be designed so that individuals from highly different backgrounds and with highly different interests can work in harmony on the same model. Gaming exercises using alternative formulations of the model for key policy variables or poorly understood phenomena, are also a useful device in clarifying issues and coordinating work. The methodology, in and of itself, aids in the creation of institutions. Data gathering and data processing is a prohibitively expensive occupation, unless it is a cooperative effort involving an institutional framework with adequate administration, individuals who know how to gather information, and who know what to gather and how to use it.

In terms of current institutions, those who would have a direct interest in the role that a simulation could play are: international agencies, the central bank, the ministry of finance, other economic agencies, the planning commissions, the universities (especially economics, political science, sociology, and anthropology), and other data gathering and statistical agencies. The execution of a large simulation for both planning and scholarly purposes probably calls for the creation of a separate institution, location of which could be as a quasi-independent operation at a university or a part of an international agency.

A final point to note is that the technological progress made in computing machinery will, in all likelihood, be of considerable importance in the solving of certain manpower and administrative problems in less-developed countries. Within the next few years remote consoles will make it technologically possible for a country, such as Chile or Peru, to afford one large computer center with many consoles in different locations over the country. The major maintenance and technical problems will thus be concentrated in one locale and can be handled by a handful of individuals. The problem of the introduction of this type of computer technology into many countries will, however, probably pose a major social dilemma. There are both many institutions and beliefs opposed to the centralization of power, which a single large computer center processing most of the vital statistics of a country appears to imply. It is my belief that the fears are unjustified but great.

SOME EXAMPLES

A few examples of simulation programs are noted
here to provide a few references and some background.
None of them can be considered to be directly concerned
with technological change per se; but all involve the
modelling of institutions and experimentation with change
in processes. Balderston and Hoggatt[7] have constructed
a simulation of the lumber industry; Kalman Cohen[8] has
simulated the shoe, leather, and hides industries;
Orcutt[9] and associates have worked on a model for the
whole of the United State economy; I. and F. Adelman
have experimented with an aggregate economic model;[10]
Holland and Gillespie have applied simulations to the
development plans of an underdeveloped economy, [11]
and Holland has attempted to apply his work to Venezuela;
Shubik is working on a model for a Latin American
country. [12] Further comments on Orcutt and Holland
are given in the next section.

The work of Shubik has been designed primarily
as a pilot study to demonstrate the value of constructing
a simulation compatible with a large data gathering
system, the system being the national income accounts
scheme designed for A. I. D. Furthermore, several
variables, such as social mobility and the long-term
effects of health, education, and welfare expenditures
on the labor force, have been introduced explicitly into
the model to indicate how such features may be made
compatible with the basic economic framework. The
modelling is relatively crude, and statistical validation and data processing have been minimal. Serious
application of this model to a specific country in depth
would require a research team and an institutional
basis.

Both the work of Orcutt and Holland have been
done in an institutional setting designed to a great
extent in coordination with the simulation. The Social
Systems Research Institute at the University of Wis-
consin is the home of the Orcutt simulation, and has,
at least by some, been regarded as a successful
demonstration of the value of simulation not only as

a methodology but also as an integrating device for an
institution devoted to social research. Holland was
able to continue his work, originally started at M.I.T.,
as a member of a small private corporation working
with a team directly in liason with a group involved
in planning for the Venezuelan government. The
evaluation of the results of this work has not yet been
made available. There were technical reasons, concerning the availability of the appropriate computational
facilities and personnel, that made the technical success
of this project somewhat doubtful; however, its mere
existence and the level of communication with and acceptance by planning personnel in Venezuela are worthy of
note.

NOTES

1. Marc Nerlove, "Two Models of the British
Economy: A Fragment of a Critical Survey," International Economic Review, VI, No. 2 (1965), 127-81.

2. Martin Shubik, "Bibliography on Simulation,
Gaming, Artifical Intelligence and Allied Topics,"
Journal of the American Statistical Association, LV
(December, 1960), 736-51.

3. See H. Guetzkow (ed.), Simulation in Social
Science: Readings (Englewood Cliffs, N.J.: Prentice
Hall, 1962).

4. Shubik, op. cit., passim.

5. For further reference see Martin Shubik
(ed.), Game Theory and Related Approaches to Social
Behavior (New York: John Wiley & Sons, 1964).

6. William Abraham, Nancy D. Ruggles, and
Richard Ruggles, An Economic Data Reporting System
for the Agency for International Development (New
Haven, Connecticut: Economic Growth Center at Yale
University, 1965).

7. F. E. Balderston and A. C. Hoggatt, The Simulation of Market Processes (Management Science Research Group, Working Paper No. 22 [Berkeley, California: University of California Press, October, 1960]).

8. K. J. Cohen, Computer Models of the Shoe, Leather, Hide Sequence (Englewood Cliffs, New Jersey: Prentice-Hall, Inc., 1960).

9. G. H. Orcutt, M. Greenberger, J. Korbel, and A. H. Rivlin, Microanalysis of Socioeconomic Systems-- A Simulation Study (New York: Harper and Brothers, 1961).

10. Irma Adelman and Frank L. Adelman, "The Dynamic Properties of the Klein-Goldberger Model," Econometrica, XVII (October, 1959), 596-625.

11. Edward P. Holland and Robert W. Gillespie, Experiments on a Simulated Underdeveloped Economy: Development Plans and Balance of Payments Policies (Cambridge: M. I. T. Press, 1963).

12. Martin Shubik, "Simulation of Socio-Economic Systems, Part I," (Cowles Foundation for Research in Economics at Yale University, Discussion Paper No. 203 [New Haven: Cowles Foundation for Research in Economics, March 1, 1966]).

COMMENTS BY KELVIN J. LANCASTER

From the standpoint of a general economic theorist, Shubik's chapter prepares grounds for the use of simulation, if one has a model of technological transfer from which to start. Building of a model, therefore, becomes the central problem to this commentator. The obvious analogy from which to build a model is probably the idea of transmission of a disease, an idea which already has been used, with some success, to study the diffusion of technology within an industry. It is possible to generalize and to extend this method into the international transfer of technology.

First, the disease has to be contracted as a disease; second, it is necessary that the other country be thoroughly infected with it. In examining this model, we must investigate, first of all, the nature of the disease; and it seems, at the outset, that there is not one disease, but a large number of different diseases to be transferred. Thus, in this context of transmission, the concept of technology as one major factor in the production function, is probably not very useful.

For operational purposes, the concept of technology must be broken into a series of activities, because it is the component activities which we use, study, and wish to transfer. Unfortunately, we know little about which techniques developed by Western countries are suited to countries with a different capital-labor ratio. Similarly, it is also doubtful whether one could transfer nineteenth-century technology to the less-developed countries. It is a myth to act as though today we could still produce things in the nineteenth-century American fashion.

Instead of discussing the types of techniques to be transferred, it would be more useful to concentrate on transfer of the technology of innovation or of adaptive imitation itself. We probably have this technology more developed in the United States than in any other country. Here is an activity that we understand well when we

propose its transfer, and I am using "activity" here in
a broad and not the usual sense of a simple input-output
relationship, or a vector of simple inputs and outputs.
It is a complex of industrial, technical, managerial
relationships in some sort of a setting. Hence, first
of all, we do not transfer technology in the vague and
general sense of simply shipping our old production
function overseas. We transfer activities as a component
of a major technology and, perhaps one at a time, perhaps in complementary groups. We transfer them by
some means; if we use the epidemiological analogue,
we would refer to these as vectors or carriers. They
carry or transmit the disease or diseases over long
distances, infecting some person in another country,
and then we very likely rely on a direct contagion
process of spreading the disease rapidly within the
country.

        The channels of transfer are various, and there
are natural carriers that effect an unpremeditated diffusion, as well as specific and direct attempts to transfer technologies. Indeed, techniques have, in the past,
been transferred, in large measure, by these natural
carriers. Capital in the physical sense, for example,
especially direct investment, has been a carrier; and,
of course, human capital, in our past, has transmitted
a great deal of technology. A good portion of our rocket
technology has been attained by the direct import of
human capital and, in some cases, movement of goods
and simple communications are carriers. Thus, one
of the questions we might consider is the extent that
natural carriers are effective in the transfer of technology; while another is the extent to which we need
to create new carriers for specific purposes.

        Once the disease is carried to other countries,
the contagion process starts, and the spread depends
on the susceptibility of the individual to the disease
and on the population structure. The susceptibility of
the individual is the question to which many scholars
have directed themselves. This broad issue really
includes the great, messy background of social,
political, and other factors that determine the degree
of acceptance of technologies. But, susceptibility is

probably also related to the complementarity of different diseases. That is, the acceptance of one
technique might make it easier to accept later techniques, and one suspects it would. A model could
probably be built around this complementarity of
different techniques.

Assuming that some degree of susceptibility
exists, the economic structure of the developing nation
is presumably going to be very important for the effective transfer of industrial technology. For example, a
monopoly may be very conservative and unwilling to
adopt techniques, but if one can break through and get
them adopted, immediate acceptance in the whole industry follows. Whereas, in a competitive small-scale
industry, it might be very east to effect quick adoption
of techniques in some firms, and although there are
competitive reasons for gradual spread of techniques
throughout the industry, nevertheless such a process
may take a long time. One suspects that diffusion
ought to be most rapid in an uncartelized oligopoly
structure, but such structure is not really typical of
most undeveloped countries. When the disease has
been properly implanted in the foreign country, the
process of transfer is successfully accomplished,
though somewhat short of complete diffusion. After
all, we never achieve complete diffusion in our own
country, if for no other reason than because the
technology becomes obsolete sooner.

After statistical data has been collected to
create a descriptive model, some thought might be
given to the optimization. The targets of the optimizing procedure will presumably determine which technology one wishes to transfer. It has been suggested
that birth control might be the best technology of all
transfers for most immediate objectives, which most
people have in mind. International trade theory
provides an important key to the optimization, though
the improved technology does not always benefit the
recipient country. In particular, if the improvement
in technology produces an effect upon an exporting
industry facing an inelastic demand, the country
receiving the technology will lose in terms of its

level of Gross National Product. If the new technology spreads in the import-competing industries, the recipient will usually gain by introducing this technology, but the result might be a potential loss to the donor country. Developing countries might find incentives to improve the efficiency in the industries supplying goods that are not produced by the industrial countries. Yet, presumably in the interest of the less-developed countries, we always attempt to improve the efficiency of their industries producing goods that compete with the exports of developed nations. In result, the countries donating the new technology are suffering losses. Therefore, I conclude, an important policy dilemma is involved in reaching decisions about the choice of technologies for transfer.

COMMENTS BY GUY H. ORCUTT

I fully agree with all the major points made by Professor Shubik, and I greatly admire the delightful manner in which he made them. My sole objective is to underscore certain points, and perhaps add a little perspective on the important but limited role of simulation. Simulation is a valuable tool, but it is only a tool. Furthermore, it is only one tool among several and it must be used in combination with others.

1. Simulation is a research tool that may be of value in studying the transfer of technology, and it may itself be a significant part of a transfer of the research technology. Simulation also may play a useful role as a teaching device as in training operators of trucks and machinery. Conceivably, simulation may be of use to policy makers, who seek insight about the likely effects of policies under consideration and try to find approved courses of action.

2. However, I think it is important that we really be quite clear about what simulation really can do for us and what it cannot. The primary importance of simulation as a research tool is that it provides a feasible way of investigating implications of models and of using models, once they have been developed. This is particularly important, because, at present, it provides the only feasible way of studying or applying models with enough realism to be useful.

3. Since simulation involves operation of a model, it will be of little value unless accompanied by a substantial effort to understand and to model phenomenon of interest and significance.

4. To be useful, simulation requires the effective use of a fairly powerful computing installation. Such a computing installation is of importance also for the development of models that are to be studied and used by simulation techniques.

5.   Any relevant model-building requires the
development and maintenance of a suitable base of
data.   In addition to appropriate development and
application of computer technology, the establishment
of a data base requires the selection and maintenance
of expedient data collection tools.

6.   Consequently, in order to become an
effective research tool for the understanding and
promoting of the transfer of technology, simulation
must be used in conjunction with several other complex
and somewhat difficult tools.   It is of the utmost importance that underdeveloped countries establish significant research capabilities of their own, which they can
direct towards their problems.   Simulation is a technology that would be useful to such countries, but it is
not the one that can be usefully transferred by itself.
To be useful, it must be transferred along with computer
technology, statistical know-how, and data collection
and storage technology.   What is really needed is the
development of entire and well-balanced social science
research institutes within underdeveloped countries.
This is an important and, I believe, feasible objective.
However, the task is a major operation, because the
transfer of several closely related and interdependent
technologies must be accomplished.

CHAPTER **6** TRAINING AND HUMAN CAPITAL

by Neil W. Chamberlain

THE THESIS

The period following World War II might aptly be
labeled the Age of Economic Development. The reasons
may be found in the impact of postwar political developments on the underlying economic forces at work. The
unprecedented involvement of people throughout the world
in a war which was unprecedentedly technological was
succeeded by an ideological peacetime confrontation of
the American and Soviet blocs, which placed a new bar-
gaining power in the hands of formerly subordinate
countries. The consequence was an incredibly rapid
breakup of former colonial empires and a concomitant
surge of nationalism. The movement was supported by
the existence of the United Nations, which was established
by the major powers, but which quickly became an instrument by which the newly emerging nations could bring
pressure for economic aid and technical assistance.
These pressures were reinforced by a quickened sense
on the part of the affluent peoples of a degree of immorality
attaching to their concentrations of wealth in a world that
was largely composed of poverty. For these and other
reasons, the theme of the age became the generalizing
of rapid economic growth.

Theories of the way to economic development have
not been lacking, each stressing its own priorities. In
some, the emphasis is on education, particularly of high-
level, skilled, and professional manpower, almost as
a supply factor that will create its own demand, providing the impetus to growth. In others, the importance of
agricultural development wins primary attention as
prerequisite to the release of resources to a manufacturing
sector. But on one point there is apparent a high degree
of consensus--that with few exceptions, a satisfactory
self-sustaining growth rate calls for industrialization.
Education and agricultural development may be necessary

147

to this end, but the objective itself--industrialization--
cannot be evaded. There is no need to examine here the
rationale for this conclusion--the avoidance of reliance
on an uncertain export trade in primary goods, the need
for high productivity outlets for men and materials made
available by agricultural improvement, the development
of new outlets for talents, which show increasing variety,
the advantages derived from external economies once
industrialization is embarked on.

If we except the handicraft industries, the industrial techniques on which the developing countries rely
must be imported from the already industrialized economies. We need not concern ourselves whether these
are the most advanced techniques or not; the only relevant
consideration is that they are advanced by the standards
of the countries that turn to them. This means that not
only must the physical capital be imported from abroad,
but that the techniques that it embodies and the skills
that are required must be taught to the native people.
The feasibility as well as the limitations of this have
long since been demonstrated--as for example, both
the proven capacity to absorb mechanical techniques,
and the proven difficulty of developing a sensitivity to
the need for maintenance of equipment. We can safely
assume that most if not all of the difficulties encountered
will be overcome with time and exposure to the demands
of an industrial system. The central thesis remains:
The dual process of expanding physical and human capital
(the latter taken to mean knowledge embodied in people)
is indispensable to a self-sustaining growth.

The developing economies have themselves
recognized this need. The internal pressures for rapid
industrialization have had their expression in imports
of equipment and training programs. "Nasser, for
example, exhorts the Egyptians to 'march forward as
one people who have vowed to work and to proceed on
a holy march of industrializing.' "[1] As Professor
Harbison points out, this "holy march" is possible
only to the extent it is led by technology designers
and technology trainers welcomed from abroad.

THE GOAL

Development as a process, or industrialization as the means, must presume some purpose. What is it that the advanced economies, which stand prepared to contribute new techniques, and the developing economies, which are the recipients, seek through this transfer? What lies behind the "development" which is sought?

The answer usually given is a rising standard of living symbolized by a growing Gross National Product per capita. This is, of course, purely a quantitative concept. By itself, it stands for an indiscriminate increase in a bundle of goods and services available for indiscriminate distribution. Behind it are either implicit or unexplored assumptions as to the qualitative content of the national product--its composition and allocation. This qualitative content, in its grossest form, may be publicized as simply more real income for everyone--more food, for example. However, if the objective is not just a temporary and illusory betterment of present living conditions but a continuing push towards a permanent economic improvement, then the qualitative content of a rising national standard of living cannot take the form of consumption goods exclusively; something must be allocated to more investment for future production. Investment by whom, for what purposes, and how to be executed become questions, the answers to which help to give qualitative shape to the quantitative target of an increase in Gross National Product. Among the issues that must be confronted are whether particular growth objectives are to be sought through the maintenance and reinforcement of existing ways of life (the strengthening of indigenous institutions) or through institutional modification, in particular the remolding of factor markets and industrial organization along lines more congenial to the efficiency of the imported techniques.

Some ambivalence in goal orientation can be expected, especially in newly independent countries in which the sense of national individuality is likely

to place special value on cultural traditions, at the same
time that a sense of urgency with respect to economic
growth increases the receptivity to practices pioneered
by the "successful" economies. The conflict in values
will be most intense in those fundamental areas that
affect the quality of both social relationships and
economic performance, such as family and work organization, career and education orientation, attitudes
towards consumption and leisure.

    The advancement of technology through transfer
cannot be viewed as possessing some autonomous value,
irrespective of the goals and values--confused and
divergent though they be--that are built into the fabric
of the receiving culture. The transfer of technology
cannot be approached only with consideration of whether
it is technically feasible; it must also be appraised in
the light of its social acceptability. This raises further
questions as to the extent to which both contributing
and recipient countries should seek to cultivate receptivity to new techniques that will change a way of life,
or the extent to which they should themselves be
guided by considerations of social values that are
found in the beneficiary country. And if the latter,
then additional questions intrude: Which values,
those of a traditional and culture-bound segment of
the society, or those of its more innovative and
opportunity-conscious members?

    Two contrapuntal tendencies assert themselves
in the traditional economies that are seeking to develop
through industrialization.   There is an insistent effort
(and need) to retain the familiar social modes of behavior,
preserving a social equilibrium and a sense of orderli-
ness and stability. But along with this goes a contrast-
ing effort and need to break up traditional ways of
thinking and behaving to give the new technological
processes a chance to take root. Some institutional
continuity is necessary for the maintenance of society
itself, but if it is so highly organized that it excludes
processes of change, it can stultify the development of
its individual members and be made self-justifying
without need for reexamination. Viable societies must
provide the opportunity for changes that can break

through an overthick institutional crust, and technological innovation, usually imported, is one common
and effective instrument of change. It may release
energies, which customary methods have restrained,
and encourage new leadership roles, which will draw
out talents that would otherwise have remained dormant.
But change can be overdone no less than tradition,
depriving a society's members of a basis for reasonable expectations of future social and economic relationships.

There are thus differing and competing values
in both traditional and new modes of social organization, but the significant consideration is that there is
value in both. Some balance, some measure of both
cultural continuity and cultural fluidity, is obviously
desirable.

If this conclusion is accepted, then the transfer
of technology can be seen as far more than a technical
and economic issue; it involves significant ethical and
political elements as well.

EDUCATION AS CAPITAL INVESTMENT

It may be a useful oversimplification to classify
transfers of technology into two categories. There are
marginal or incremental imported changes that are
attached to existing institutions or behavior patterns.
These represent an improvement in the efficiency of
the old forms without destroying them. No one is
adversely affected, no one is subjected to cultural
shock or strain, or at the worst any adverse effects
can be rather easily accommodated or offset.

In contrast, there are transfers of technology
that are socially disruptive. In order for the new ways
to be effective, they must break up established ways
and values, and impose new economic and social, perhaps also political, insecurities. Such disruptive
effects may occur on a large or small scale; they may
be attributable to major single programs or to the
cumulative effects of a number of lesser activities.

They may be concentrated in particular industrial
sectors or geographical regions of the economy, or
more generally distributed throughout it. It is only
with such disruptive technological innovations that
this chapter is concerned.

The quantitative goals, which are usually
posed in the planning-for-growth process, invite
technically efficient solutions. This is true, whether
one starts with the most macroeconomic goal (a rate
of increase in Gross National Product, such as the
5 per cent rate per annum recommended for the
developing countries over the U. N. "development
decade" of 1960-70), or the more particular, but
still aggregative, objectives of a specified rate of
increase in the amount of rice grown, or tons of
bauxite mined, or kilowatt-hours of electric power
generated. The technically efficient solution represents a choice from among a number of alternative
technologies available from the industrialized nations.
The selection of technology carries with it a choice,
too, of the kind of training that is functionally necessary.
Trained personnel, capable of carrying on the operations that are technically called for, become part of
the process which is being transferred. We speak now
of such personnel training as the creation of human
capital, and we view the creation of human capital
as a necessary accompaniment of the creation of real
capital, on which the growth target depends.

By treating human capital as analogous to physical
capital we encourage the implicit assumption that train-
ing--and ultimately the educational system as well--should
be looked on as part of an economic production function,
determined by the imported technology and without much
respect (even occasional lip service) to the contemporary
cultural values. The approach to training and education,
at least at the lower levels, tends to become mechanistic
and functional. Even with respect to higher education,
impatience with the spawning of disproportionate numbers
of nonfunctionally educated and relatively useless holders
of college degrees has caused planners to emphasize the
desirability of awarding opportunities for advanced
training to those who are pointed in the direction of

particular professional skills, the importance of which
can be established with reference to the country's economic plan--agronomists, engineers, physicists, economists, and the like.

Professor Webster Cash, testifying to this
general orientation out of his experience in Rhodesia
and Nyasaland, writes that

> the most basic difficulty of proposals
> for high-level manpower planning in
> New Africa . . . is their mechanistic,
> demand-oriented view of economic
> development. The proposals treat
> economic development as though it
> can be explained by the presence or
> absence of knowledge or skills, capi-
> tal, labor, and natural resources.
> Since labor and natural resources are
> given, development results from balanc-
> ing investment in education and other
> investments in human capital with
> investments in tangible capital. [2]

Similarly, Professor Hla Myint, whose experience includes involvement in Burmese educational
administration and economic planning, comments:

> Logically, one might expect a great up-
> surge of a liberal educational policy
> encouraging individualism, enterprise
> and innovations to break down the rigid-
> ities   both of traditional and of the
> colonial systems. But, given the pre-
> vailing intellectual view that such quick
> change can be forced through only by
> economic planning, the prevailing bias
> is against both economic liberalism and
> "liberal education" in favor of detailed
> skilled manpower planning integrated
> with programmes of technical education
> which ideally should specify the exact
> type of training and the exact number
> of trainees. [3]

This view of training and education as a form of
investment (human investment) which complements
capital equipment, leads very easily to a conception of
the former as a necessary extension of the latter. This
view is not confined to the underdeveloped economies;
understandably, it guides the aid-distributing countries
as well. Without appropriately trained nationals, aid
embodied in physical capital would have little value.
"An integral part of the assistance to developing countries under the U. S. aid program is technical training
given to 'participants' from the various nations, either
in the United States or in a 'third country.' This training of nationals abroad helps develop the human resources
needed to make maximum use of other forms of aid such
as commodities and equipment, financial assistance and
technical advice."[4] Here again realism appears to
demand that a choice of techniques determines the type
of training and education to which members of the
developing society will be exposed. Investment in
human capital follows naturally from, and its form is
shaped by, a prior determination of investment in
physical capital. [5]

WEAKNESS OF THE HUMAN CAPITAL CONCEPT

The treatment of education as an investment has
such apparent validity that one hesitates to probe its deficiencies. After all, every concept has its weaknesses,
which do not necessarily rob it of analytical value or
operational usefulness. For example, it has frequently
been pointed out that education is a consumption as well
as an investment good, something that is wanted for
itself and not because it is an instrument for acquiring
something else. This justifiable criticism is scarcely
relevant to the underdeveloped economies, however,
and need not detain us here. In a country which is hard
pressed to find the means for supporting any educational
effort at all, it would be quixotic to challenge the use of
investment rather than consumption criteria in determining the direction of its limited educational effort.
Criticism must run deeper than this if it is to be relevant to the circumstances of a society seeking to
extricate itself from poverty and stagnation.

A more telling weakness is the operational difficulty of applying the concept, and the dangers of serious misdirection of scarce resources in attempting to apply it. If we grant that educational expenditures are a form of investment, then this invites--indeed, almost necessitates--some attempt to measure the return on that investment. Otherwise, the concept reduces simply to an interesting broad-scale rationalization for whatever action a government chooses to undertake in the training field--however much or however little. To be given significant substance requires that it be possible to make some determination as to whether additional investment in primary schools is preferable to fattening the budget for higher education, for example, or whether more money pumped into training people is preferable to allocating the same sums to, perhaps, improving the agricultural yield through irrigation or subsidies for chemical fertilizers.

The difficulty of measuring return on investment is something that has deterred many American business firms, often with a panoply of experts, from making any serious effort at precise relative evaluation of expenditures even on physical capital equipment. To do so requires estimating the probable stream of returns from the alternative possibilities. That, in turn, depends on judgments as to possible changes in consumer tastes and producer technologies, developments in product and factor markets, developments on both the domestic and international political fronts, and a variety of other unpredictable contingencies. The figures that are attached to any particular investment possibility have less and less content, the further one projects into the unknown future. Surmises can be made, informed judgments and expressions of intent, but these are scarcely the basis on which quantitative estimates concerning a variety of projects, usually made by different people, often with special interests that affect their calculations, can be credited with a rigor and finality that permits comparison and determines choice.

It is in large part for this reason that many American business firms rely on a simpler calculation of "payback"--the period within which an investment

will be recovered. Generally speaking, the shorter the
payback period, the higher the ranking of a project on
the list of alternatives. The quicker the recovery, the
less likely that the uncertainties of the future will inter-
vene to undermine the value of the investment, and the
greater the opportunity to reinvest in other ventures
similarly promising quick returns.

Even this simpler if grosser approach does not
avoid a basic danger inherent in the return-on-investment
concept as applied to the educational expenditures. Whether
one stresses a short-time horizon and makes use of a payback approach, or thinks in terms of a discounted stream
of returns stretching into a farther future, the investment-
in-human-capital concept urges a more precise calculation of values. The greater the risk and uncertainty element,
the less precise can be the calculation of returns. The
surer the pay-off, the more attractive is the investment.
This is particularly the case if the resources are so limited
that mistakes in their use have a high opportunity cost.

Educational investment, as part of the development
process, takes two quite different forms, with markedly
dissimilar time dimensions and risk content, but each is
necessary to the other. On the one hand, there is the
vocationally and professionally oriented training geared
to specific technological needs, in which the pay-off seems
surer and quicker. On the other hand, there is the
education pointing towards longer-run institutional
changes--with the social matrix setting and conditioning
the value of technology--in which the return is much less
certain and the pay-off often doubles.

This latter category includes more general educational programs, which concern themselves with the social
and political prerequisites for a modern economy, which
develop a capacity for invoking the means and analyzing--
anticipating--the consequences of social change, which
encourage basic literacy and logic as tools that are
relevant not to the specific jobs or functions but adaptable
to changing conditions. ". . . The real trouble (in the
underdeveloped economies) is not merely a shortage of
specific skills, but a more general and pervasive lack
of skills and abilities to digest, absorb and diffuse the

modern technology. "[6] The spread of these more general but pointedly necessary skills is in part a matter of educational content and in part a matter of institution building, with each drawing on and encouraging the further development of the other.

Vocational training, to provide a development base, must be accompanied by more fundamental changes in social systems, which can only be fostered by rather basic institutional changes, which in turn require a calculated educational strategy with a very speculative payoff.

The point can perhaps be made clearer by going back to the proposition that the human-capital proponents have themselves emphasized--that investment in physical capital requires complementary investment in people to be made effective. Reversing the proposition, we can also say that the return on such investment in people cannot be measured without ascertaining how their education is to be used. We can think of an "investment unit" that has as its components both human and physical capital, each of which lends value to the other, without which neither has economic value. The steel mill or the chemical plant is only a public monument until it is complemented with people who can make it work, just as a technician is only a pair of unskilled hands in the absence of capital equipment that complements his skill.

The same kind of "investment unit" occurs in institutional development. To create political and social forms requires investment in the form of buildings, equipment, public information systems, even salaries and other current operating expenses of much of governmental activity, which from one point of view constitute long-run investment, since the day-to-day operations of a government can be directed to changing people's attitudes, opportunities, and actions in ways that purposively affect the future. But to create new political and social forms requires, too, a complementary investment in the education of people who can be counted on to devise such programs and make them work.

The value of the latter educational investment can
only be measured in terms of the long-run pay-off of the
institutional forms that are being created. But the
uncertainty of such a return is likely to give it a lower
rating in the government's investment schedule than
short-run, more technically geared and apparently
certain "investment units, " and a lower rating, too, in
the estimation of equally impatient aid-giving countries.
The consequence is to give emphasis to projects that
have a quick return, even if they do not provide much
of a basis for a development path or a sustained growth
pattern, and to deemphasize investment in institution-
building that is essential to continued growth but has no
immediate pay-off.

The focus on education as investment in human
capital has given further--and sophisticated--support
to an already present tendency to stress the quick
returns from technical and vocational education.
Technology and science have such an objective and
neutral coloration that one is predisposed to believe
that they can flow freely into any culture and transform
it, as they have transformed the countries of their
origin. [7] Initial resistances can be overcome by the
demonstrably superior results. Obsolete customs
will give way before modern methods. The transfer
from one culture to another is almost like the transfer
of some higher truth, the proof of which has already
been established by the fact that it has "worked" elsewhere. Investment in this form is relatively sure and
secure.

In some cases a belief in the inexorable impact
of modern technology may be warranted, but in other
instances its effectiveness is undercut by the slowness
with which social patterns are modified to accommodate
the development process. Even in those instances in
which a transplanting of technology is carried off more
or less successfully without much thought to a prior
preparation of the institutional soil, side effects of
human dislocation, resentment, and actual suffering
may, over time, jeopardize the social and political
stability on which any long-run development depends.

THE MORAL AND PHILOSOPHICAL ISSUE

If the possibility exists that cultural resistance and barriers will impede the effective transfer of technology, the opposite possibility is also present: Even with lags, the new systems may have their impact, overriding traditions and customs and forcibly molding a society that is congenial to their functioning. There are those who speak of the "industrialization process" as having a homogenizing effect, ultimately transform- ✓ ing all societies into more or less common patterns.

> The pre-existing culture must adapt or be broken as industrialization proceeds. Industrialization imposes its own cultural patterns on the pre-existing culture. ... Regardless of the resistance or acquiescence of the old culture and the tolerance or intolerance of the industrializing elites, the pre-industrial cultures sooner or later are largely modified or swept away and new cultures take their place; new cultures more compatible with the new technology; and much of the anguish of men and institutions that marks our current period of history derives from this transition from the old to the new. [8]

Such a view accords with the conception of science and technology as constituting some objective and uniform body of ideas having objective and uniform applications, so that once taking root, the tree of knowledge grows into the same shape wherever it is planted. This conception avoids any moral or philosophical issues as to whether the result is desirable by regarding it as necessary.

Other individuals, whether or not subscribing to a doctrine of inevitability, take the position that in the face of grinding poverty, with lives literally lost for lack of food, and brute instincts encouraged by the desperate struggle for mere survival, morality is on the side of forcing the adoption of modern techniques,

whatever resistances traditional cultures may offer. If
life has value, and if the development of human decency
requires some minimum economic underpinning, then
even pressures to bulldoze through the acceptance of
modern imported industrial methods have their ethical
justification.

Both of these rationalizations are open to question. Industrial systems that have proved themselves
efficient in Western contexts do not, for that reason,
have any objective claim to the same efficiency in other
cultures. For one thing, efficiency must be gauged in
terms of objectives, and the relevant objectives are
not simply productivity in given operations but the
whole package of preferences--social as well as eco-
nomic--that are held by a people. A production system
efficient in one country may be less efficient in another,
because--even with the same output per unit of input--
it is destructive of values that are important to the
second but not to the first.

As a second consideration, even if one views
efficiency in a purely limited input-output sense,
such efficiency--which is the only purportedly "objective" justification--may fall for the reasons we have
already noted, so that primitive cultures remain
immune to growth despite islands of limited technical
efficiency scattered throughout their ocean of poverty. [9]
A virus of industrialization does not somehow spread
contagiously, despite hyperbole sometimes suggesting
that it is so.

Industrial efficiency might be furthered if,
instead of relying on perfected but exotic technologies,
both the knowledge-exporting and knowledge-importing
countries joined in seeking to create new production
processes expressly geared to conditions found in the
developing economies. However science-based it may
be, technology is a social phenomenon, and has no
single economic value attaching to it or remaining
constant as it crosses cultural boundaries.

The survival-and-decency line of argument has
obvious merit, but it can be pushed too far. While the
dead have no values, the living do. There is no ethical

answer to those who would rather be poor on their own
terms than better off on someone else's imposed standards, or even to those who ask assistance but refuse to
pay for it by conforming to another's values. If survival
is necessary to the furtherance of one's own set of
values, is mere survival sufficient to assure the latter?
Even in the face of extreme poverty, it can reasonably
be argued that the qualitative nature--the purposes--of
economic growth deserve specific recognition along
with its quantitative aspects. A rate of increase in
Gross National Product cannot be accepted as a sufficient target in itself; we require information as well
concerning its composition and the costs of achieving it.

        This line of argument does not carry with it any
lurking implication that the transfer of Western technology to developing economies always exacts too high
a price in the form of cultural shock and social dislocation. It has already been noted that at least some
elements of a society are likely to benefit from induced
changes, and that adaptation to change may be of greater
long-run social value than resistance to change. The
only point being made is that the value of any transfer
of technology--both with respect to an ex ante appraisal
of the possibility of successful transfer, and an ex post
evaluation of the actual results--must embrace more
than a measure of the increase in output of the good in
question; it warrants explicit consideration of the qualitative impact on society, in terms of that society's own
complex of values.

        Such explicit consideration is especially important
where the idea of education as investment in human capital
has won acceptance. One might argue, with technical
validity, that in measuring a return on educational investment all such longer-run and more qualitative effects
can be allowed for. But, precisely because these are
qualitative, they do not readily lend themselves to
measurement, and are likely to be omitted, because
they cannot be impounded in a measurable return. The
investment analogy leads to (or, at a minimum, supports)
policy conclusions based on the simple premise that a
higher return from one type of education stamps it as
superior to another kind of educational program yielding

a lower rate of return.   This seemingly innocuous and, indeed, apparently self-evident principle is almost certain to lead to a vocationally oriented educational system. Only training which can be effectively utilized deserves to be capitalized, and only those forms of education having a capital value are viewed as alternatives in the choice process.

From this perspective, which admittedly is etched more sharply here than is commonly the case, education becomes an instrument for shaping the individual to the economic needs of his society. We recognize the need for higher education to cope with advancing technical and scientific knowledge, for example, largely because that seems necessary for career development within our kind of economy.   Educationists as well as economists are beginning to look twenty years ahead to the kind of training that will be necessary in the kind of economy we anticipate by then, so that we can adjust our educational system to the evolving needs of the economy.   There is admittedly a good deal of merit in carrying through such an exercise; education and training have usually had relevance to economic needs--understandably, since economic activity represents such an important facet of our lives.   But, carried to the point where the technical requirements of a society dictate the character and intellectual content of the culture, it constitutes a dubious molding of individuals to suit the needs of the system.

The danger becomes great, to the extent that one consequence of such an outlook is to create a new cultural elite--the technically educated--who are themselves understandably predisposed to technical solutions.   The "technocrats" become a political force whose guiding principle is efficiency in the mobilization of resources.

Efficiency is, of course, nothing to be despised. As soon as one posits objectives, one cannot afford to be unconcerned about the efficient use of limited resources to achieve the goals that have been set.   The central problem comes in the identification of those goals.   Where these are defined in quantitative terms--a rate of increase in Gross National Product, the highest return from among

alternative investments in education, a stepped-up
productivity in the manufacture of electricity--technical
efficiency is likely to dominate the planning process.

CONCLUSION

The purpose of this chapter has not been to
discourage the attempted transfer of technology from
the advanced to the developing economies, nor to urge
that technical innovation be restrained or paced.
Technological change has immense value in breaking
through the crust of tradition and opening up opportunities for individual initiative and creative drives by
those whom the culture previously inhibited. It is the
only basis on which now retarded economies can premise a brighter future.   The accelerated drive for
economic development, which has characterized the
postwar period, has, however, tended to overstress
the technological and industrial aspects, perhaps because progress in these areas has been so spectacular
in the already developed economies. Ambition and an
emulatory propensity in the underdeveloped economies
have joined with philanthropy and international politics
in the advanced countries to encourage this stress on
transfer of technology.

It is in light of this tendency that this chapter
puts forward two principal propositions:

1.   Technical change is embodied in a social
context that it both affects and is affected by.   The
economic efficiency and the social value of a production
process in one setting is not automatically or necessarily
transferable to another setting.   The effects should be
anticipated and evaluated in terms of the society into
which the change is being introduced, not in terms of
the society from which it comes.   The fact that a home
government requests specific forms of technical aid
does not warrant a belief that such an evaluation has
actually been made or absolve the aid-giving country
of ethical responsibility for making its own independent
evaluation.

2.   The conception of education as investment in human capital has the danger of bringing further support to those who seek quick returns through vocationally oriented training in industrial and professional skills. The rate-of-return concept encourages the more certain and shorter-run pay-off, and deemphasizes the need for educational programs looking to institutional changes which, while more speculative and longer-run, are essential to the sustained growth.

The question raised and conclusions reached in this chapter may seem excessively philosophical and even remote in a world that is basically composed of poverty. Nevertheless, while I would be unwilling to abandon present technical assistance programs, and would like to see such programs expanded and improved even within the limited framework of their own assumptions, it does seem to me that there is value in exploring the fundamental premises on which our facilitating technological role rests. Not least of all because whatever answers we reach, however tentatively, may prove relevant within our own society.

NOTES

1.   Quoted by Frederick Harbison in C. A. Anderson and M. J. Bowman (eds.), Education and Economic Development (Chicago: Aldine Publishing Co., 1965), p. 232.

2.   Webster C. Cash, "A Critique of Manpower Planning and Educational Change in Africa," Economic Development and Cultural Change, XIV (October, 1965), 40.

3.   Hla Myint, "Social Flexibility, Social Discipline, and Economic Growth," International Social Science Journal, XVI, No. 2 (1964), 258.

4. Final Report, Evaluation Survey of the Korea/
U. S. Participant Training Program, 1955-1960 (Washington, D. C.: Department of State, Agency for International Development, September, 1963), p. 1.

5. The "human capital" concept can also lead
to a quite different policy conclusion, as Alexander Kafka
has suggested in his "Discussion" in the American
Economic Review, XLIX (May, 1959), 172. "If
human and physical capital are admitted to be close
substitutes over a very wide range (rather than complementary), we can explain in part the propensity of underdeveloped countries for large-scale ultramodern projects,
since there so much organization is, as it were, built into
the machinery and can be imported along with it, to replace
a lack of organizing ability which reflects deficient human
capital. "

One can accept this proposition only with major
reservations. First, although it is true that "ultramodern"
technology dispenses with the need for a number of specialized skills, as automated processes in Western economies
have demonstrated, experience also demonstrates that
such advanced technologies increase the dependence on
other skills, particularly for maintenance purposes. The
question then becomes whether the skills displaced or the
skills required by the advanced technology are easier for
the underdeveloped country to come by. Second, although
in given circumstances advanced technologies may substitute for human capital, they cannot do so across the board,
for economic as well as technical reasons, therefore the
view of training and education as necessary complements to
physical capital (ingredients of the country's production
functions) remains as the general rule.

6. Hla Myint, "The 'Widening Gap' of the Underdeveloped Countries: A Critical View" (New Haven: Yale
University Economic Growth Center, 1965), p. 12.
(Mimeographed.) I have benefited greatly from conversa-
tions with Professor Myint, who fortuitously was in resi-
dence at Yale during the period when I was preparing this
chapter. My theme had been developed before I became
aware of his similar views but has profited from exposure
to his thinking.

7.   There is at least a hint of such predisposition in the suggested creation of a "world bank of knowledge" on which developing countries may draw. The New York Times, November 30, 1965, reported such a recommendation emanating from the White House Conference on International Cooperation, convened by President Johnson.

8.   Clark Kerr, John T. Dunlop, Frederick Harbison, and Charles A. Myers, Industrialism and Industrial Man (Cambridge, Massachusetts: Harvard University Press, 1960), pp. 94, 97.

9.   Professor Wilfred Malenbaum has called attention to what he considers a basic error of Indian economic strategy--a belief that a modern industrial sector will "pull" the more backward sectors, including agriculture, along with it.   He observes that this belief has been proved to be false in the fact, and argues that what is necessary is a major "push" directly in the more traditional parts of the economy, especially agriculture.

"Unfortunately, the United States and other developed lands have little expertise on generating an economic revolution among vast millions of persons still bound in the complex of a long-static social and economic order.   The task is primarily indigenous.   Its first ingredients must be a major research offensive, to discover what is the pattern of life in these backward sectors, and particularly what actual threads do (or might) tie them more closely to the modern sectors. " From a letter to the Editor of The New York Times, January 2, 1966.

COMMENTS BY JACK BARANSON

Emphasis in our aid programs over the past fifteen years has shifted from (a) investments in physical capital, to (b) technical assistance, to (c) the need for institutional change. Permit me to comment separately on the elements of Professor Chamberlain's hypothesis.

1. Institutional change and education (as distinct from vocational training) is necessary in order to increase a developing society's ability and willingness to introduce technological change.

My comment: Probably not true.

I incline toward Professor Svennilson's view that both technological change and institutional change are most likely to proceed hand in hand. Professor Chamberlain's master plan involves reeducating a society that will devise and install new institutions receptive to socially harmonious technologies--to say nothing of the Realpolitik of putting men with newborn rationality in circumstances that will permit the implementation of change. Here, the problems of design and execution would seem to be formidable--somewhat akin to social engineering the Renaissance or the Reformation.

A program of institutional change for the villages of India that is fundable would be worth looking at. I would be interested in how one cultivates attitudes toward quality control in a mas o menos society beyond prescriptions to "change the value system." Also, much more can and should be said on how to educate and train more effective problem-staters and policy-makers in the engineering, economics, and, yes, even sociology of development.

2. There is a need to choose and adapt technological systems according to ethical and human values.

My comment: Yes, but...

    I somehow have the feeling that Professor Chamberlain's emphasis on moral and philosophical consideration shares some of sociology's old bent for seeking to preserve a basic harmony and stability in society. The fact is we are dealing with poverty pockets and social stagnation that calls for ferment and change. I don't think peasant societies will be sweetly reasoned into transition, nor that change will come from a Platonic wind that reshapes cultural values. More probably, change will emerge from the kinds of incongruities and impasses that the new technologies introduce into traditional societies. In most cases the choices are between ethics and survival.

   ✓ 3. The concept of education as investment gives undeserved support to technocrats and places a premium on quick returns.

My Comment: Not necessarily.

    The fact is, judgments have to be made at national and local levels on general resource allocations as they relate to growth objectives--apart from what may be termed "social horizon" goals. Here, the concept of investment and return serves a useful operational purpose. Professor Chamberlain implies that this utilitarian approach will lead to too much short-term pay-off training and not enough long-term education of socially useful capability. Actually, decisions have to be made on the amount of resources to be allocated to dams and the amount to schools; and within educational budgets, the amount to general education, and the amount to vocational or on-the-job training. The problem is analogous to allocation of research and development resources between basic research and applied and development fields. Good allocation implies a portfolio mix of long-term growth stocks and short-term speculative issues that promise quick capital gains. Quick pay-off investments are not to be spurned in economies on the subsistence margin. The development of techniques that measure more accurately pay-off will not, in and of itself, narrow the vision of analysis.

Fritz Machlup has provided some useful, conceptual guidelines on the balance between long-term investments in knowledge and its relationships to applied research and on-the-job training. [1] There are some worthwhile guidelines on the innovational role of certain institutions in Margaret Mead's work. [2]

4. There is a need to choose and adapt technology to social and economic environment.

My comment: Amen, but let us not overdo a good thing.

Unquestionably, much more can be said and done about designing products and systems for the low income economies and limited supplier capabilities. Again, I incline toward the functional rather than ethical. I personally think the logistics of long production runs in small-scale societies is more important than culturally harmonious housing products or factory designs. I do think cultural and behavioral factors are critical in such areas as birth control pills and cheap proteins.

5. Lending nations should share moral responsibility with developing countries on their technological choices.

My comment: A touchy question.

C. P. Snow has commented on this question of moral philosophy for emerging societies in Africa. Africa, said Sir Charles, has had enough of St. Francis Xaviers and Albert Schweitzers. They want technicians to muck-in, do a good job, and get out.

I am inclined to think our role in emerging societies is as pathologists, rather than moralists.

NOTES TO COMMENTS

1. Fritz Machlup, Production and Distribution of Knowledge in the United States (Princeton: Princeton University Press, 1962).

2. Margaret Mead (ed.), Cultural Patterns and Technical Change (New York: Columbia University Press, 1955).

COMMENTS BY JOHN W. KENDRICK

I shall first comment on the final section of Professor Chamberlain's chapter.   There he raises the moral and philosophical issues posed by the imposition of industrialization patterns on preexisting cultures.   He points out that increased per capita income is not the only criterion of efficiency--other values are at stake, and account must be taken of the social costs of material progress.

One feels that Professor Chamberlain is making only a passing and largely futile gesture to these issues. His own values favor ". . . breaking through the crust of tradition and opening up opportunities for individual initiative and creative drives by those whom the culture previously inhibited. " Seeing this as a "brighter future" clearly reveals his own "Faustian" value system. I am not an anthropologist, but I suspect that individuals are generally happier and more contented (or "better adjusted"), almost by definition, in primitive or relatively static societies, despite "inhibition" of initiative. But there is little purpose in an argument on this score. The leaders, at least, of most less-developed societies have embraced material progress as a goal. The important issue is that it be pursued as intelligently as possible, with awareness of the costs and the need to minimize the adverse qualitative impact of social change. As Professor Chamberlain puts it, a balance between cultural continuity and cultural fluidity should be maintained.

As I see it, the disruptive concomitants of economic development can be held down by trying to tie the required new values onto old values. Every culture has a variety of mores and attitudes, some of which are more favorable to change, and others less so. The trick is a selective emphasis on traditions that are favorable, and a downgrading of adverse values. The process of selective adaptation is facilitated if the leaders do not force the pace of economic advance too rapidly. In particular, dogmatic attempts to break the old and impose new patterns carry a heavy cost

and may boomerang by strengthening covert resistances
that can impede efficiency for generations. I gather that
Chamberlain considered the general type of education he
advocates as an alternative to forceful, disruptive
attempts to alter institutions in an effort to accelerate
economic progress.

I would like to hear more from Chamberlain as
to the content of the general education program he envis-
ages, and how widespread it is to be. As far as the
education of potential leaders is concerned, I would hope
that it would be a truly liberal program which would
include study of economics, political science, sociology,
social change--and so on. In other words, the goal
would be to build broad knowledge and understanding in
the potential leadership, in the hope that it would bring
the wisdom to build the necessary institutions for economic development while preserving the best of received
values. Certainly, the social costs of material progress
would be far higher if the future leaders received a narrow
Marxist indoctrination instead of a liberal education.

One must also keep in mind that the very processes
of technological development, and the expansion of the
industrial and urban sectors, relative to the rural and
agricultural, are effective vehicles of cultural change.
Perhaps education does not have to carry as heavy a
burden in the process as Chamberlain implies.

With regard to Chamberlain's chief argument, I
think, we can agree as to the importance of general vis-a-
vis vocational training, while still adhering to the view of
education and training as a form of investment. All he is
really saying is that one cannot measure the prospective
returns on human investment very accurately, and that
he believes the return on general education may be very
much higher than is apparently believed by planners and
responsible officials in many developing countries.

Few, if any, economists seriously contend that
one can accurately estimate prospective rates of return
on various types of human, as well as nonhuman invest-
ment--although the work of people like Becker and
Schultz has been ingenious and plausible. But the

approach of viewing all forward-looking outlays as
investment is a useful framework for appraising expenditure plans. Even if expected rates of return are
expressed in terms of rough orders of magnitude, with
pluses and minuses assigned to qualitative elements and
uncertainties, the systematic exercise is a useful background for decisions which, in the end, will be judg-
mental in any case.

        In fact, I would advocate appraisal, in an invest-
ment context, by social scientists and planners of all
proposed outlays that would significantly enhance future
output- and income-producing capacity. This means
not only tangible business investment in structures,
equipment and inventories, but also household and
governmental tangible investment. It would cover
intangible investments--not only vocational and general
education, but also research, development, and engineering outlays, health and medical expenditures, and mobility costs. In the final analysis, all types of investment
are competing with each other for limited savings, and,
in total, are competing with consumption. It is impossible to plan for educational and training expenditures
in total, and by type, without considering all the other
alternative investment possibilities.

        I would also suggest that investment planning
budgets include the cost of creating tangible human
capital--that is, the expense of rearing children to
working age, a type of investment that looms large
in many less-developed countries. Creating human
beings is as much investment as producing plant and
equipment, since the quantity as well as the quality
of both human and nonhuman capital enter production
functions. To some extent, the expense of rearing
children may have an abstinence effect on parents.
But, to an important degree, rearing costs compete
with other forms of investment, including the training
and education of youth. In countries with high birth
rates (and especially if they have passed an optimum
man-land ratio with the given technology), the rate of
increase in productivity and per capita product would
be enhanced by investing less in producing bodies,
and investing more in equipping the labor force with

more and better tools, education, training, and health
care.

To summarize, I agree with Professor Chamberlain's emphasis on the need for more general education,
but I do not believe its neglect is a necessary result of
using investment criteria in development planning. It
has been due rather to inadequate analysis of the possible
returns to institutional innovations facilitated by general
education, as well as by the very process of industrialization, and other forces. Certainly, Chamberlain's
cogent analysis will help redress the balance.

As long as an investment analysis framework is
not employed narrowly and mechanistically, I would hope
it would be expanded to include all developmental outlays.
As Chamberlain himself points out, we must consider
the composition of Gross National Product as well as
its rate of growth in development analysis. Certainly,
identifying all investment-type outlays, budgeting for
each of these separately, and giving adequate weight
to their relative importance and the resources available
for nonconsumption generally, are essential to a systematic development effort. A gradual relative increase in
total investment, in appropriate proportions, is surely
essential to promoting the transfer of technology and
for growth in per capita real incomes generally. The
investment calculus should not be discarded as a tool
in this endeavor merely because it may be misused.

CHAPTER 7 THE STRATEGY OF TRANSFER

by Ingvar Svennilson

The problem of the transfer of technology is one
of the most important in the world today. In the economic
sphere, it is the problem. At one extreme, we have
populations of the rich countries that live in relative
luxury in a push-button world. At the other extreme, in
underdeveloped countries, we have poor people who are
underfed and toiling under the most primitive technical
conditions. As we must assume that the human mind is
the same in both worlds, that knowledge can be abundantly
reproduced, and that it can be transferred with a minimum
of cost, it may seem a paradox that differences in technology between various parts of the world cannot be
evened out easily and rapidly.

Actually, our experience shows that in the process
of transfer there is a time element involved that far exceeds
our earlier expectations. While earlier we were optimistic
enough to think that technological change would progress
over years or decades, we now tend to resign ourselves to
the fact that we are faced with a problem of secular adjustment. In view of the population explosion, this slowness
of technological transfer becomes a very serious problem,
because starvation, disaster, or even premature death is
threatening the poor countries, if the transfer of technology
cannot be accelerated.

In the first place, this applies to the technology of
food production. Studies in various countries have convinced me that soil and climatic conditions in the poor
countries, on the whole, are potentially so good that the
agricultural production could be increased to meet the
needs of the double population and allow for a considerable rise in food consumption standards, if modern
technology were applied. However, the population will
double within the next twenty to thirty years in many of
these countries. Can modern agricultural technology
be transferred in such short time? Or, if we cannot

175

increase food production in a few decades, can the technology of birth control be transferred so rapidly that the
population's demand for food can be balanced against a
limited supply?

One may be less pessimistic about the possibilities
of transferring industrial technology within a limited time,
even when one considers that in the past years the process
of industrialization has not progressed very far compared
to the enormous task. In any case, the problem of transfer
of technology today is primarily one of speed. The main
question is: Can the transfer of modern technology occur
within a few decades instead of as a long-run secular
process? In order to approach this problem we should,
of course, carefully study the basic conditions for transfer
of knowledge in its scientific, psychological, pedagogical,
sociological, economic, and organizational aspects. But
the emphasis should be on the time element involved. Only
in this way will our research correspond to the operational
needs.

When we speak about the transfer of technology,
we should be aware that this is a process that integrates
a large number of elements. A high degree of complementarity exists between these elements, which means
that if one element is missing, the other elements will
be useless, or their effectiveness will be highly reduced.
We may divide these elements into three broad categories,
each of which is very complex. To establish modern
technology in an underdeveloped country, we need to
change:

a. social systems and human attitudes;
b. knowledge and human skills;
c. the physical implements in which modern
     technology is embodied.

In each of these elements the process of change tends
to be slow. It may, however, not be equally slow in all
respects. We face, therefore, the problem of development
bottlenecks. There does not exist, however, a general
pattern of bottlenecks, common to all underdeveloped countries and to all sectors of their economies. The location
of the main bottlenecks of development differs. In some

cases, equipment that represents modern technology
is not available. In many cases a modernization of
agricultural technology will not take place even if
fertilizers, irrigation, and tractors are available,
because human attitudes and social systems offer
resistance to change. In other cases, there is no scarcity of people with an adequate education, even the
necessary capital equipment may be available, but
the managerial skill may be missing. Evidently,
the location of the bottlenecks should decide our strategy for development. In order to speed up the process
of technological transfer we must first break those
bottlenecks that offer the primary resistance to change.

   The problem of strategy is, however, complicated by the fact that development is interrelated in
the three indicated respects. Improved knowledge may
lead to revolutions in human attitudes and social systems.
I think that there is also much to be said for the Marxian
materialist view that the availability of implements
embodying modern technique will change human attitudes
and social systems. We know far too little about these
interrelations; they form a very important field for
future research.

   The fact that such interrelations exist must
evidently be taken into account when we choose our
strategy for transfer of technology. The best solution
may be not to attack directly the bottleneck that seems
most obvious, for example, education. It may be that
the attack that yields the most rapid result should be
directed towards other elements, because it may bring
a more rapid widening of other essential bottlenecks.

   According to one school of thought, we should
start with the social and political reforms. Evidently,
the theory of Communism is to start with a revolution
and we must admit that often it has been successful.
We may ask whether there are other possibilities of
reforms of a more democratic kind, which will create
results within a short time?

   Many believe that we must start with the education and the development of skills, and that an introduction of modern technology before that stage has been

passed is useless. This pessimistic view expects
significant results only in the very long run. A closer
study of the problem will show that the interrelations
between various elements in the development process
extend in all directions. This speaks for an integrated
approach which attacks all elements at the same time
and in which a change in one respect supports changes
in others. I shall illustrate these possibilities by two
examples, the first from agriculture, the second from
industry.

Many abortive attempts have been made to
introduce modern technology--irrigation, fertilizers,
improved seeds and breeds, new methods of cultivation, better storage, and improved marketing--in the
thousands of villages in India and Pakistan. Systems
of extension services have been established, covering
the whole area.   The supply of agricultural inputs
has been organized and often subsidized, with negligible effect.   Assistance of foreign experts has also
often failed. The cultural, social, and economic
structure of villages and the lack of education have
offered resistance to the technological change.

The experiments at the Comilla Agricultural
Center and Academy in East Pakistan provide an
example of a new successful approach.   The main
characteristic of the center, which extends its activities over a large agricultural district, is that the
approach has been integrated, i. e., all aspects of
development have been attacked in a coordinated way.
Thus, introduction of modern methods of agricultural
cooperation on strict economic lines has been combined with organized saving, a credit system which
eliminates money lenders, joint management of tube
wells for irrigation, organized supply of farm inputs,
storage and marketing of farm products, and tractor
stations with repair shops.   The activities of the
center extend to adult education for farmers, mullahs,
and midwives from the villages.   Formal education
is combined with demonstration and training on the
experimental grounds of the center.   Agricultural
techniques adapted to the local conditions are developed
on these grounds with the assistance of foreign experts.

It is the leadership and management with democratic roots in the agricultural society that often have
been lacking in projects for the agricultural development. Such leaders cannot be replaced by bureaucrats
sent out by the central government, or by foreign
experts. In the Comilla experiment much emphasis
is put on the cultivation of leadership in the village
cooperatives, and in the larger units. An academy
for advanced training of leaders and co-op managers
is attached to the center, which combines formal
education with training in the nearby agricultural
station. The idea is that those who have been trained
at the academy will go out to serve as leaders of new
centers in other districts. This dissemination process
has now been started.

Let me shift to industry. The most successful
examples of the rapid transfer of technology are found
in the activities of the subsidiaries, which are established by Western firms in underdeveloped countries.
In such cases, often it has been possible, even in backward countries and within a few years, not only to
establish a modern industry but also to make it operate
effectively. The last point is important, as industries
in underdeveloped countries usually produce at high
costs, in spite of low wages and modern equipment.
This is one reason why they cannot compete in the export markets.

The characteristics of transfer of technology
via subsidiaries may be outlined. The activities are
not restricted to advice by experts or to blueprints
drawn by consultants. The parent firm with all its
specialists acts as a team that takes part in actual
operations. In this way, not only published technical
knowledge but all the know-how and skills of the
parent company are transferred to the new unit.
Education of domestic labor takes mainly the form
of training-on-the-job. Especially important is
that the entrepreneurial capacity of the parent
company helps to integrate the various elements
of an effectively producing unit. The assistance
extends from blueprints to construction, training,
management of production and marketing.

I have mentioned these two successful examples
in order to illustrate some features of a strategy for
transferring technology in an effective and rapid way.
First, both examples represent the integrated approach,
combining efforts to change the social framework of
production with improvement of education and training,
and with the introduction of modern equipment.   To
arrive at this point, a strong leadership is needed.
It cannot be provided by specialists in one facet of
production, who are usually available without difficulty.
It can be done by education, technical or of other types,
or by inviting a selected group of foreign experts.   The
main point, however, remains, even if all other personal
elements are available, that good leaders and managers
are trained by experience.   And it is natural that such
experience does not exist before prototypes of modern
technology have been established.

As to industrial management, enormous funds of
entrepreneurial experience and skill exist in the developed
countries.   These resources have been tapped only to a
small extent for technical assistance.   A largely unsolved
problem remains: how to mobilize these resources.   It
can only be done, with moderate success, by establishing
subsidiaries of parent companies in the developed countries.   Often parent companies lack commercial interest
in such operations, and, to a large extent, underdeveloped
countries prefer domestic or even state ownership.   There
exist, however, various possibilities of partnerships
between domestic and foreign interests which have been
widely experienced.   In my view, even a minority interest
of the assisting foreign firm in the venture is of a great
advantage, because it provides a guarantee for efficiency
in the joint operation.   If such partnerships are not
acceptable to the receiving country, there remains the
possibility of entering into management contracts.   One
of the most important but unsolved problems of technical
assistance is how to induce Western firms, in all industrial fields, to take on this kind of management activity,
even if it does not coincide with their business interests
as producers.   Technical assistance is financed mainly
by governments, partly through international organizations.   The solution seems to be that governments or

international organizations enter into contracts not only
with individual specialists but with private firms, to
establish and manage new units in underdeveloped countries, regardless of whether such operations are combined with part ownership.

A second feature of the examples I mentioned
is the team approach to the transfer of technology.
Each enterprise combines a large number of different
types of technologies and skills. All technology is not
included in textbooks, nor can it be reproduced in
written expert advice. For efficient application of
technology, a wide range of know-how must be added,
and the technology can be transferred easily by personal contact, demonstration, and training. Each
specialist carries his bits and pieces of know-how,
but the efficiency of enterprises depends highly on
the teamwork of many specialists who possess
complementary knowledge and skills. The conclusion is that the most efficient transfer of technology
takes place through teams of experienced specialists
participating in actual operations. The result may
be called a pilot project.

It is evident that pilot project teams, which
take part in actual operations, cannot spread over
such a big surface as is possible for more-specialized
or general advisors. Therefore, within a given framework of assistance we must choose between concentrated
efforts on a limited number of complete pilot projects
and a more-widespread diffusion of specialized technical knowledge. An important problem of strategy
is: On which type of assistance resources should we
concentrate? The answer is probably that we must
have both. More-widespread diffusion of knowledge
may prepare the ground for successful actual operations. However, expert blueprints for the underdeveloped countries, in most cases soon being
covered with dust, create an impression of waste
and a lack of balance in the efforts. One may ask
whether the transfer process would not gain in
efficiency and speed if more resources were concentrated on pilot projects carried out by teams of
experts?

The effectiveness of this approach will depend on
the diffusion process that originates from the pilot project.
We cannot rely on the assumption that the diffusion takes
place by itself. There are methods, such as used in the
Comilla case, whereby the diffusion process can be intensi-
fied and accelerated. The organization of the diffusion
process within the underdeveloped countries is one of the
most important aspects of the transfer of technology.

A third lesson which I would draw from my two
examples is that training in operations and learning-by-
doing are superior methods for transferring knowledge
and skills needed for the application of modern technology.
Formal education in underdeveloped countries is, usually,
of low quality, because it often clings to the textbook
wisdom, which is remote from application. This is
natural in a world in which prototypes of modern technology
hardly exist. The products of textbook education, even
if of the desired specification, are, therefore, often useless in actual operations or have a low efficiency. As
a rule, those who are employed in a modern unit have
to be reconditioned for the actual jobs. A low level of
formal education can be supplemented by training-in-
service. Even an illiterate man can learn to drive a
tractor or handle some types of modern machinery.
Adult education can be organized in an agricultural
center or at a factory in close contact with the operations. For these reasons, one should not be doctrin-
aire about the thesis that general formal education
should precede the transfer of modern technology. Both
could proceed, hand-in-hand, in such a way that the
transfer of technology is accelerated.

Finally, social change, new attitudes toward work
and technology, and education and training may be promoted
by introducing equipment that embodies modern technology into an underdeveloped milieu. This seems to
be the most effective way of accelerating the transfer
of technology. It may mean that one should increase
the introduction of modern labor-saving equipment in
a system with abundant supply of labor. However,
scarcity of capital will establish a limit to such a
policy, and one may have to restrict oneself to
pilot units or a partial mechanization. In the Comilla

case, electrical pumps for irrigation and a few tractors were introduced, while most work was performed with simple tools. The use of tractors had an economic justification, because they could till deeper than oxen and plows. Tractors could break hard, dry soil, and the period of transition from one crop to the next one could be shortened, enabling a switch to a three-crop system. However, the use of electrical pumps and of the tractor has brought far-reaching psychological and social effects in the village. A man on a tractor develops a different outlook from one who stays behind slow oxen. Village life must be organized in a new way if the farmers have to take joint responsibility for electricity distribution and pumping equipment. The new agricultural technology breaks the conservative traditions, and similar results are achieved by introduction of modern equipment in an industrial plant.

It cannot be claimed that elements of modern technology will alone do the job; adequate management and leadership are needed. One must try to adjust the human factor by education and training to the conditions of modern technology. If this is not done, the modern equipment will not be used effectively and will be soon run down. Moreover, as has often been the case, the unit of modern technology becomes an isolated island in a traditional society which even may deteriorate socially and morally as a result of the backwash of modern technology. Much more energy should be spent on intensifying the social and cultural diffusion effects of the units of modern technology that are introduced in backward areas. This is a problem of organization and policies, which, I admit, is extremely difficult to solve. We must learn from all the mistakes that have been made, and try to find new roads for progress.

In summary, the theory that it is necessary to wait for the slow process of education and corresponding cultural and social change to mature until the time becomes ripe for the introduction of modern technology is not correct. With adequate leadership, with more team operations instead of specialized advice, with education and training integrated into the modern

operations, and with a careful organization of the economic, social and political adjustment of the society
to the conditions of modern technology, I believe that
the transfer of technology can be highly accelerated.
In this way, the supply of capital equipment may tend
to become the main bottleneck. However, technically
speaking, it is easy to break this bottleneck. Success
depends only on how much of our financial resources
we are willing to give up in order to aid the underdeveloped countries.

I certainly do not claim that it is easy to solve
the various social and human problems that must be
attacked in such an integrated approach. Many mistakes
will no doubt be made, because failure, inefficiency, and
social maladjustment probably cannot be avoided. I
maintain only that the problems could be solved with such
success that the transfer of technology would be greatly
accelerated.

CHAPTER 8 SUMMARY: DISCUSSION OF ISSUES AND CONTROVERSIES

by Daniel L. Spencer
and
Alexander Woroniak

The two decades following World War II brought a major change in the evolution of economic thought. Dynamic and controversial problems of economic growth were thrust upon the new generation of economists, as suddenly every nation was painfully pressed to reconstruct, to broaden, and to diversify the economy in order to meet the needs of an increasing population. With the help of two postwar prodigies, applied mathematics and the computer, economists forged powerful analytical tools and instruments of economic policy. The concept of economic planning and a new set of institutions involved in developing a national economic policy became the subject of vigorous research. Possibly the fact of the rapid recovery of Japan and Germany, despite their devastated physical plants, focused attention on the importance of technological knowledge and the role of its diffusion and transfer for the growth of output. Undoubtedly, however, Jacob Schmookler is correct that "it was our renewed interest in economic growth that led to the rediscovery of the importance of technological progress."[1]

One major aspect of technological progress-- the transfer of technology and understanding the multiple channels through which technology moves from one point to another--is not only new to the economists. It is also controversial, and poses serious problems of identification, quantification, and analysis. However, there are concrete advantages in our ability to consciously direct, stimulate, and adapt technology developed for one specific purpose to other uses or to transfer it from one locale to another.

It is the purpose of this chapter to summarize and analyze some controversial issues evolving from

different interpretations of the nature of technological
transfer to developing countries, and its role in stimulating the social change that must accompany economic
growth.   The controversy covers not only the description
and evaluation of the importance of various channels of
technological change, but extends to the interaction of
various factors that affect the transfer mechanism.
This chapter is based on the discussion that followed
presentation of the main topics at the Airlie House Conference.   It is divided into six sections, each prefaced
by a synopsis.   In each section factual and theoretical
views are exchanged; and participation of other social
scientists helps to "keep the economists honest. "

        "Transfer of technology, " as used in this book,
should not be confused with "the diffusion of technology. "
The latter term has long been used by anthropologists
and other social scientists (note the pioneering study
of Everett Rogers)[2] to denote a kind of natural process
whereby cultural traits (technology being one) flowed
from one cultural milieu to another.   Rejection or
absorption depended on the strength of the propensity
to import change from outside the system.   Anthropologists often contrasted diffusion via imitation and innovation with the independent invention, just as present-day
students of technological change contrast the borrowing
of know-how with an indigenous research and development effort.   In short, the term "diffusion" referred to a
spontaneous process.

        In contrast, "transfer of technology" incorporates
an additional, specific element, which typically has not
been utilized in studies such as Rogers', i. e. , planned
and purposive type of action.   This purposiveness
manifests itself by conscious, predetermined effort
and commitment of resources to transplant technology
from one country to another, or from one use to another.
In a world seeking shortcuts to economic development,
it becomes extremely advantageous to plan technological
intake in a more premeditated manner.   Thus, the concept of transfer takes on a purposive meaning in the
context of development and growth problems.

RETROSPECT AND PROSPECT

Synopsis

Controversy about the problem of the capacity to absorb new technology resulted in a Methodenstreit between two schools of thought. The broad socio-institutional approach to the analysis of absorptive propensity was presented strongly by Dr. Murphy and his commentators. To the socio-institutional group, the transfer of technology is almost equivalent to rapid industrialization and major social change, and, therefore, their view of the transfer is very complex, entangled with other problems, and almost impossible to achieve without revolutionary turmoil. However, very interesting illustrations were cited by the scholars who do not seem to attach such importance to the analysis-in-depth of underlying cultural and social infrastructure. The latter concentrate on the operational problems of raising the level of comprehension of illiterate workers, or promoting viability of newly established loci of new technology. The operationists focus on such practical problems as information gathering, promotion of imitation, and stimulating entrepreneurship. It is unfortunate that not enough research has been directed toward the step-by-step operations of transfer, and, consequently, pressing questions of men concerned with actual operations remain largely unanswered.

Specific Issues

The need for policy guidance in the transfer of technology to Africa was stressed by Dr. Samuel C. Westerfield, Deputy Assistant Secretary for African Affairs, U. S. Department of State. He and his colleagues tend to the opinion that not shortage of capital, but limited capacity to absorb the new technology is the chief hindrance to development. For some scholars, this is the ultimate question: Is there a possibility of technological transfer without revolution? While it is recognized that the cost of revolutionary changes is fantastically exorbitant, and the final outcome

unpredictable, the experience of countries such as Chile
does not encourage much hope for other possible solutions.
Scholars pointed out that Chile suffers from a socially
retrogressive tendency and socio-institutional stagnation
in spite of adequate natural resources and a nucleus of
technology. Dr. Shubik found that: "By definition, any
entrepreneurial spirit or activity in Chile can be traced
to relatively new arrivals (Europeans and Middle Easterners)."

     Professor Richard L. Meier came forward with a
concrete plan of operations for a "continuous long-term
transfer of technology." His proposal includes first, a
legitimating agency, usually a government, or some other
body, whose authority is accepted by at least some part of
the population. The central feature of the plan is the
creation of a set of informational and promotional agencies
which serve as a two-way transmission belt for the transfer, seeking and gathering new ideas from outside, and
providing catalytic assistance to embryonic entrepreneurs.
The condition is the development of an a priori set of
templates for various types of viable organizations based
on the new technology. The fourth element is the location
of entrepreneurs, and fitting the templates to the business
operations they wish to establish. The fitting is a long
process, which goes through many stages before production
starts, i. e. , recruiting personnel, analysis of markets,
establishing informational background, and so forth.
Finally, when the production stage is reached and a surplus developed, this surplus must be plowed back into
the economy, which might be a foreign economy. In fact,
this is the case of Chile--here, the surplus of natural
resources was fed back into the world at large, and
Chile is only now, belatedly, retrieving some of the
benefits in terms of foreign aid. The gist of Meier's
plan is the introduction of new technology into the native
economy via templates developed by information-gathering
and promotional agencies, and fitted to entrepreneurs
and their activities.

     Meier also suggested that a programmed instruc-
tion, similar to the much praised military training,
should be designed and suited to illiterate or virtually
illiterate people. The military programs of World War II
and the postwar period point the way. Such programs,

applicable to pers ons with zero to four years of education, and using television, radio, and visual aids, must
convey modern ideas, modern behavior, and modern
techniques.

Some scholars regard the transfer of people,
or immigration, as a simple and ready solution to the
transfer of technology problem, because of the insignificant appearance of entrepreneurial talent in the indigenous cultures. Others, however, cite the case of
Is rael, pointing out that the incorporation of immigrants
into the local system can only be achieved in twenty or
thirty years under optimum conditions. An influx of technically advanced immigrants would result only in the
creation of local enclaves.

Once more, the role of the Protestant ethic in
the development of the entrepreneurial spirit and in training disciplined and reliable labor was emphasized by
Meier's illustration of Puerto Rican and Virgin Island
experience. He attributed the great success of the plastic
container industry in Puerto Rico to the surplus of "young
men who understand machinery." Availability of
machinery-minded workers, willing and able to work in an
environment alien to their culture, is one basic precondition of the successful transfer of technology. Most
scholars, however, agree with Professor Rosenstein-
Rodan that "one does not have to be a Protestant to
develop." Modern sociology, psychology, and psycho-
analysis seem to exaggerate the problems involved in
technological transfer. The experience of four or five
big industrial empires in São Paulo provides enough
evidence that growth is possible, in spite of bottlenecks
like lack of skilled labor and managers. Entrepreneurs,
often of foreign origin and uninhibited by local tradition
and welfare regulations, were able to develop a reliable
labor force by selecting only 10 per cent of the labor
turnover and by training them on the job, and thus
created highly viable industrial concerns.

Dr. Teitel found the clue to Puerto Rican development in the availability of cheap labor, combined with
access to the American free trade area. Growth of
Canada, too, has a similar explanation. In contrast,

Teitel's own country, Argentina, is well supplied with
people trained in all kinds of skills, but the crucial
obstacle to growth is a limited market. A limited market
has implications for problems of scale, monopoly, foreign
competition, oligopoly, collusion, and exports. Professor
Rosenstein-Rodan added that promoting regional integration
and widening import facilities in developed countries are
priority matters that must be solved if transfer of technology is to be effective.

Dr. Adler, summarizing the experience of the
World Bank, expressed serious doubt whether the
adaptations of new technology to labor supply and scarcity
of skills are really as important as some economists
claim. International Can Company in Nigeria introduced
the most advanced equipment and trained unskilled
workers in a remarkably short time. In three years of
operation, the Nigerian plant achieved the highest productivity of the company's many plants throughout the
world. The adjustments necessary to meet the technical
requirements of the country's artifacts are much more
complex. Dr. Adler gave several illustrations, including
the case of kenaf (Hibiscus cannabinus), a hard fiber.
Considerable research was required to obtain the right
machinery for processing this new resource before it
could be utilized. He differentiated between technological
adaptations that must be made before operations are
started (purely investment-decision problems) and those
like adjustment to the supply problem that normally are
met after production starts.

ECONOMIC THEORY

Synopsis

Kmenta's pioneering attempt to develop a theoretical framework for the analysis of technological transfer was both praised for its ingenuity of the technological
gap concept and criticized because of its assumptions. The
validity of assumptions underlying the linear homogeneous
production function was seriously questioned by a number
of economists and social scientists, who stressed the

complexity of the forces involved in the transfer operation and the various important but delicate factors that
are hard to squeeze into any formulation that assumes
linear relationships.

Specific Issues

Relevance of the neoclassical framework for
the theoretical analysis of technological transfer was
seriously questioned by Professor Rosenstein-Rodan,
because of the omission of realities in the production
function, such as the economies of scale, and because
of lumping together of skilled, unskilled, and semiskilled labor. The semiskilled workers, the sergeant
majors of the production process, are the critical
bottleneck; their scarcity exceeds that of capital in
developing countries. Consequently, it seems rational
to transfer the most modern, capital-intensive technology to the low-income countries, because it requires
relatively few semiskilled workers.

However, on the subject of choice of techniques,
the views differed significantly. Dr. Salin cited the
Israeli experience to support his thesis that the most
advanced technology is unsuitable to developing nations.
Logically, early capitalist type of equipment is preferable, at least in the initial stage of the development.
Probably the ideal type would be some modified version
of technology adaptable to changing conditions in underdeveloped countries.

Dr. Kranzberg summarized the common view
of noneconomists that empirical data do not support
neoclassical analysis that simplifies complex relationships to a few variables with unwarranted emphasis
on the capital formation. Shubik agreed that vital
factors left out of the first order homogenous production function include "management, the whole concept
of structure, the whole concept of information, the
whole concept of entrepreneurship," but he emphasized
that the concept of the technological gap introduced by
Kmenta is a promising tool of economic analysis.

Professor Meier brought attention to one specific factor that might seriously inhibit innovational activities in developing countries--the lack of significant information necessary for decision-making. In fact, he estimated that the information available in developing countries about markets, industrial relations, quality control, product acceptability, etc., represents less than 10 per cent of the information used in the United States for similar decisions.

SCHUMPETERIAN THEORY AND CONTINENTAL THOUGHT

Synopsis

The opinion that Schumpeterian ideas may not be relevant for a modern, operational concept of transfer of technology and that the key role in the technological transfer must be given to sheer imitation seems to prevail. The case of Japan is thought to be unique, but studies of other comparative cases, such as Taiwan and Hong Kong are recommended. However, an opposing group feels that large, revolutionary changes are required in non-Western societies for effective induction of technology. That is, major structural shifts in the socio-economic fabric must precede or accompany the absorption of technology borrowed from the West.

Both the imitationist school and the cultural revolutionists tend to merge the transfer of technology into the broader concepts of social and institutional change, but the imitationists seem to see the problem of transfer of technology as a fairly concrete operational one, and search for operative levers, such as producer entrepreneurs, promotional bodies, science, research and development, turn-key plants, and the role of the military. The revolutionists are more ready to muddy the waters, and mix the transfer of technology with industrialization, cultural change, and larger, long-run problems. They tend to be concerned more with the impact on the donee (though impact on the donor was considered briefly), and also to endorse specially

designed, labor-intensive technology for transfer. The
imitationists are fairly tough-minded, holding that the
exigencies of the problem dictate transfer of technology
in an "as is" condition.

Specific Issues

Professor Murphy questioned the sufficiency of
transfer by imitation. He indicated that transfer of
technology is basically an innovative process, because
it requires conveyance of a whole system of arrangements such as business organization, financial, and
market mechanisms. Adler wondered about the
meaningfulness of the general Schumpeterian hero of
economic history to the theme of transfer of technology
to the less-developed countries. There is no lack of
able entrepreneurs in most developing countries who
are successful in distributive trades. The real problem
is how to convert them into producer-type entrepreneurs.
The distributive entrepreneur lacks managerial ability,
technological information, and the realization of the
importance of technical efficiency.

Salin suggested that the two types of technology
transfer must be distinguished. There is one set of
problems involved in the transfer to nations with an
adequate scientific and technical base, and thus, capable
of absorbing and building on the introduced technology.
On the other hand, the conditions of some underdeveloped
countries require a different theoretical approach and
analytical treatment, because of limited technical capa-
bility.

Numerous cases from India, Brazil, and Nigeria,
stated Dr. Rogers, provide ample evidence of the crucial
role of military training for the developing of entrepreneurial attitudes. In fact, veterans of military service
represent an important, if not the only, loci of technical
know-how, change, and entrepreneurship in these countries. These veterans are the carriers of innovations
into local communities, and if their attempts are not
successful, it is often not the failure of the men, but of
the innovation. Professor Svennilson contended that

the "institution of promotion" has not been given adequate
attention. If one does not want to study the whole chain
of activities involved in transfers of technology, one should
look into the promotional function. Thus, both Rogers
and Svennilson see the importance of a sponsorship function
as a catalyst in developing entrepreneurs.

Rosenstein-Rodan dismissed the melodramatic
role of invention and innovation, because humble imitation seems to be of greater relevance to the technological
transfer. It is not innovation that matters, but the spread
of identical facilities; twelve turbogenerators are more
important than one turbogenerator. The drama lies in the
multiplication by imitation. In regard to the choice of
technology for the labor-intensive economies, engineers
at the Massachusetts Institute of Technology could hardly
believe Rosenstein-Rodan was serious when he sought
to interest them in a capital-saving technology. Although
only modern, large-scale plants should be transferred,
this does not exclude subcontracting opportunities for
small-scale firms.

Different but no less complex and formidable are
the problems challenging donor countries in the transfer
of technology on an international level. Dr. Piquet felt
that it was important to take into account the structural
changes in the donor country attendant on the transfer
of technology to developing economies. Thus, the willingness of a donor country to import the products of the
transferred technology competing with the donor's less-
efficient industrial sectors is essential to the transfer
process.

Another leading issue, the role of basic science
in a country that receives the advanced technology, was
raised by Dr. Price. He pointed to analogues with big
industries and big organizations including the military
in the United States, and noted that these are science-
oriented, therefore, fundamental research makes sense
to them. Is there an opportunity for science to play a
similar catalytic role in the less-developed countries as
in the major American industries? Dr. Spencer indicated that science has two major roles in the less-
developed countries: One is backstopping in the sense

that the basic scientists act as a kind of court of last
resort for the choice of the technology to be introduced.
Second, science is essential to the receptive technological base of the donee country. Economists from
developing countries often had criticized the allocation
of scarce resources to the training of scientists who
seemed to be less essential than workaday engineers
to the technological transfer. However, Spencer held
that the basic scientists are farsighted, selective agents
whose international prestige could often offset uninformed
bureaucratic judgments on the desirability of technological
borrowings. Moreover, specific research on Japan
suggested that expenditure on scientific research was
highly correlated with technological transfer. [3] Dr.
Nelson added that the technical developments "coming
down the pipe" could be better incorporated by the
industry in the borrowing country if science and scientific
research were present there. As the research and development effort in the United States and other donor countries
tends to cause rapid obsolescence of the transferred technology, it pays to build in a scientific and technical research competence in the donee country to keep the turn-
key plants viable and competitive. The pressing need for
the buildup of indigenous centers of science and innovation in the developing countries was emphasized.

Dr. Salin was gratified that imitation had been
singled out to highlight the transfer mechanism, and
underscored the copying of technology as a long established
channel of transfer. Imitation, he thought, leads to
consequences utterly unforeseen over the long run in
both the donor and donee countries. In particular, donor
countries must carefully foresee the consequences of their
actions as, for example, the United States' present balance-
of-payments problem, which partially stems from the
massive donations of technology under the Marshall Plan.

THE SOCIO-ECONOMIC VARIABLES

Synopsis

The validity and usefulness of the concept of technological transfer were evaluated from the theoretical and

empirical points of view. Concrete advantages and potential applications of this new tool of economic analysis were
formulated although with certain reservations on specific
theoretical grounds.

Controversy about a basic issue arose when two
distinct viewpoints, a "Gestalt" position and a "transfer"
position were contrasted. The former concerned itself
with the adaptative milieu within the recipient country,
urging the necessity of adaptation of the technology to the
donee's cultural and social "Gestalt," while the latter
position was concerned with the operative problem of
transfer, leaving the adaptation problem to take care of
itself. The polarities may thus be oversimplified: On
the one hand, technology must be adapted to the indigenous culture; on the other, culture must adapt to the
foreign technology.

Specific Issues

Dr. Nelson raised the fundamental question of
the acceptance of the concept of technological transfer
as an economic tool on theoretical grounds. First,
he offered formal arguments based on the neoclassical
theory, questioning the validity and the need for such
a concept. This position was echoed by Professor
Ferguson, who pointed out that the established body
of neoclassical equilibrium embraces the problem of
technology transfer. Within a framework of factor
proportions, rates of remuneration to factors, price
ratios, and other relevant economic variables, the
mechanism of adjustment across international boundaries would automatically take care of the transfer of
technology, wherever such an opportunity arises.

However, Nelson dispelled the challenge effectively by indicating that the differences in factor
endowment, remuneration, and many other equilibrium
factors do not explain the difference between the economies; and that, on the principle of Occam's razor,
it is sensible to assume that a gap in the level of
technology can be closed by planned, massive trans-
ferral of specific kinds of knowledge and technique,

as in the case described by Spencer[4] of the transfer of
the aircraft industry technology to Japan. "Inflow of
generalized skills" which might result in response to
the price mechanism is not as meaningful and operationally effective as "exploring this powerful policy handle
which may be seized, " i. e. , the transfer of technology.
Thus, the issue of the validity of the transfer of technology as an economic tool was resolved. Dr. Siegel
observed that the scope of the transfer mechanism is
very broad, and in addition to patents and other commercial channels, includes many alternative means of transfer such as technical missions, exchange of students,
books, and journals.

The central issue, choice of techniques for the
developing countries, remained unsettled. Professor
Villard indicated his strong preference for those techniques especially designed to meet the factor proportions in the developing country. Teitel maintained
that the underdeveloped countries do not intend to develop
or adapt their own techniques, but are going to borrow
and imitate the latest techniques drawn from a vast
reservoir of the available technologies of the advanced
countries. According to Professor Kendrick, big pay-
offs may exist in research and development directed to
adapting the transferred technology to the specific needs
of the donee country.

The argument of the "Gestalt" position was syn-
thesized by Dr. Shubik. Modern technology could be
transferred to Englishmen without destroying their
"Gestalt, " but the massive introduction of modern
technology into Latin America would not only be destructive to the indigenous culture   but likely to fail
due to conflict with a "Gestalt" inhospitable to Western-
type technology. Salin commented that the "Gestalt"
of the Japanese people does not seem to be in great
danger from a huge infusion of Western technology.

TRANSFER OF TECHNOLOGY
AND SIMULATION STUDIES

Synopsis

The relevance of the simulation to the transfer of technology problem has not been completely clarified, though its superiority over straight, analytical techniques of the kind offered by Kmenta was inferred. Yet, one is left with a vista of an operationally possible, large-scale approach to the technology transfer problem in the future via simulation models, though concrete application still must be demonstrated, and further research is mandatory.

Both Dr. Shubik and the commentators emphasized the general nature of the simulation more than the specifics of its application. Few concrete examples of the actual use of simulation were cited, except the simulation of a diffusion of an innovation described by Dr. Rogers. His study of the diffusion of innovation at the micro-level in a small Latin American peasant village, using an epidemic model, and his references to other social scientists and quantitative geographers are very interesting. A laudable contribution was made by Dr. Orcutt, who described the need and advantage of the establishment of data centers and securing an adequate data base. This suggestion combines the institutional approach with mathematical precision.

Specific Issues

Simulation often has been criticized as a "sandbox for scholars," Dr. Rogers admitted, although it is a favorable technique of the research sponsors. Shubik thought that there had been an oversell of simulation in some areas, quoting the Forrester articles in the <u>Harvard Business Review</u>, [5] which could conceivably have done more harm than good. "The Forrester simulation and its methods were suited for a world that has no logical switches... no distributive time lags, and not many things that are essentially the bread and butter of modelling that most of us are faced with. "

The advantage of simulation methods over straight
mathematical techniques is particularly important in
cases in which the nonlinearity of relationships makes
it difficult to solve the model analytically.   Normally,
Dr. Kmenta explained, one turns to simulation studies
if the problem is not amenable to the technique of the
ordinary mathematical models, especially if the relationship of the variables is curvilinear.   Orcutt con-
firmed that simulation is less restrictive than analytical
techniques, which are likely to be so constricting that
they impede interdisciplinary research.   Simulation
allows the researcher more freedom to do what is necessary to grapple with the subject.   Shubik cited the example
of economists working with anthropologists to prepare a
data base for the quantification of facts on the urbanization
problems.

According to Professor Svennilson, the true
estimates of the partial relations are an essential component for the building of a simulation model.   Orcutt
agreed that typically about 5 per cent of the total effort
involves the operation of the simulation model, the bulk
of 95 per cent is used to build the statistical data base,
which includes mainly these partial relations.   Shubik
also concurred with the idea of developing a simulation
model from subsystems,   but added that the problem
of validation of the components is not as serious as
sometimes thought.   He argued:

> The point that is important in
> simulation studies, and in fact, in
> decision system studies in general,
> is not that it is necessarily a virtue
> of itself to spend all of your re-
> sources in measuring the propensity
> to consume to the ninth decimal
> place.   A question, which is meta-
> theoretical for some purposes, that
> you may wish to ask is: If I could
> measure the propensity to consume
> beyond a certain level of accuracy,
> how much more would it buy me in
> terms of the model in which I am
> interested? Does the decision which
> I wish to make depend on the sensitiv-
> ity of that part of the system?

TRAINING AND HUMAN CAPITAL

Synopsis

It is evident that the destructive effects of a conflict between the indigenous, traditional culture and foreign technology developed by people of alien, Western milieu worry many scholars. Some honestly believe that a precondition of transfer is the promotion of institutions that facilitate a gradual absorption of technology. Many, however, dismiss the problem of environment, and accord priority to the immediate importation of the latest Western technology. A typical representative of the latter group is Dr. Teitel, who conceded that he is willing to build institutions along with factories, but he is unwilling to trade even a little factory for a major institutional buildup.

An attempt is made to broaden the transfer of technology concept to a grandiose extent, perhaps much beyond any operational use. Some social scientists tend to merge the transfer of technology with the questions of political decisions, revolution, "who benefits," etc. But pragmatists, with a less drastic view of technological change, seek to untangle the transfer of technology problem, and confine it to defined, manageable proportions.

Specific Issues

The successful transfer of technology obviously poses serious problems and difficulties for both donor and donee countries. Even if one agrees that the native culture must adjust to the rational, machine-dominated technology, the unanswered question is: How can the process of change best be accomplished? Rosenstein-Rodan pointed out the conflict between two objectives, high productivity and equality of opportunity, embedded in attempts to "maximize the welfare function." He held that substitution and trading between these two objectives are possible. Although he admitted that the "Gestalt" position has some interest, he urged partial "differentiations" of the "Gestalt" in respect to the selected variables in order to arrive at decisions within a socioeconomic system.

Shubik added that two areas of economic theory cause misconceptions: the production function concept, and welfare economics. The welfare function, in mathematical terms, leads to logical inconsistencies as certain well-known paradoxes have shown. Shubik argued that the crucial question is: Who benefits from the development?

> The reason why I say this is that one
> cannot build rigidly decent models
> that change the emphasis that is often
> talked about in the welfare theory. We
> talk about that lovely surface, or what-
> ever it is that we are assuming, that
> everybody in the society is in an isola-
> tion box, and then confront them with a
> series of binary choices over every
> possibility in the society. Whereas, in
> fact, we have dictatorships; we have
> political bodies; we have the institutions
> that end up with some group being in
> control of the society. One thing which
> we do not face up to is... how many
> revolutions we are willing to interfere
> with? How many revolutions are we
> willing to sponsor? What are the prices?

Thus, Shubik concluded, even on theoretical grounds one is forced into an institutional point of view, because the economic theory is an in abstracto theory which does not deal with the administrative mechanisms needed to carry out policy.

Svennilson pointed out that much of the technology transferred is neutral in relation to the cultural milieu and requires little social adjustment, but that another large category of techniques is nonneutral, or is such that the borderline between these two classes can be shifted by social engineering in the less-developed society. One can consciously develop society in different ways around the new technological element. However, Sven-nilson thought, there is a definite advantage in having a real psychological break by opting for social discontinuity.

Chamberlain replied he might accede to the inevitability
of cultural discontinuity, but cultural dislocation should
not be the contribution of the Western donor. He pleaded
for an attempt to engineer and develop proper kinds of
institutions as part of the growth process, rather than
relying simply on injections of technology to less-developed
countries. The former approach, according to Chamberlain, citing the success of Yugoslavia, was a surer basis
for a sustained growth pattern, and would allow donee
countries to achieve growth in terms more compatible
with their own cultural values.

Other scholars felt that although Chamberlain's
main theme might be supported on ethical and logical
grounds, its practicability is another matter. Anyhow,
some thought, his example of Yugoslavia, as an illustration
of successful experimentation with institutional reforms
that presumably take root in the indigenous culture, is
not very convincing. Kmenta asked what was the criterion
by which Chamberlain measured success. What were the
figures for the Yugoslavian Gross National Product and
the growth rate? Chamberlain thought that it was too
early to test for statistical pay-offs, but that the current
growth rate had been good. Kmenta concluded: "So for
that story, the criterion amounts to one of a value
judgment." Hoselitz pointed out that Yugoslavian income
had increased 5 or 6 per cent, but whether the growth
was attributable to education, or institutional rearrange-
ments, is another matter.

Current literature offers ample evidence that the
controversy about the ways to change the attitudes in
less-developed countries in favor of social and technical
change has not been resolved. Rosenstein-Rodan illustrated the optimist's and pessimist's views of how to
modify the "Gestalt" by quoting Dr. Samuel Johnson: "If
a man is about to be hanged, it clears his mind wonder-
fully," and also George Bernard Shaw's epigram, "If
you wish to change a man's attitude, you must change
his grandfather's." However, as his grandfather is
probably dead, "you work on his father," Rosenstein-
Rodan added. Meier described an action proposal,
developed by his students, which might assist in altering
the socio-institutional environment in the underdeveloped

countries. A United Nations University, its faculty
composed of foreign scientists, should be created to
provide education for foreign students, who, in turn,
would be obligated to return home and spread their
newly acquired ideas and technology.

The case of Argentina, according to the scientists who studied her recent progress, provides evidence
that the levers of education and institutional changes are
less relevant than Dr. Chamberlain claims. Argentina
for many years experienced one of the highest levels of
literacy in the world with free education from grammar
school through the university. However, Dr. Teitel
agreed with Professor Svennilson that the industrial
plant serves as the carrier of skills and modern practices required for rapid growth. One might want to
disrupt the indigenous milieu as fast as possible, by
incorporating modern techniques, practices, and skills.
Problems of desirable control of the pace, style, and
quality of the social disruption can be efficiently met by
proper social engineering. Dr. Baranson praised the
idea of encouraging business enterprises "by changing
some of the administrative rules to give them the further
nurturing that they need to. . . get them on their way."
International Business Machines in Argentina was a good
example, which, if multiplied, would get the country on
its way.

Indicators of social progress and the measurement
of economic growth are a subject of great interest to
scholars. Meier drew attention to the indexes of political
development, which have been used for the last three
years as a supplement to the economic measure of per
capita income. These indexes appeared in the political
science and sociological journals, and Meier thought it
possible to discern a substitution between economic
development and political development. Since education
is a major tool in stimulating and creating social
communication in a society, investment in education
would probably have a greater reward in terms of a
political index than in any index of economic development.
The level of political development is very important as
an antecedent to the economic development in terms of

the concept of legitimacy (legitimating agency), which he
had previously enunciated. [6]

Both educators and economists are engaged in the
controversy whether--and to what extent--education is a
consumer or investment good. Shubik related his experience with kibbutz managers who deplored the exodus of
the university graduates to the cities, but acknowledged
that only 5 per cent of the jobs in the most luxurious
kibbutz required university graduates. The managers
regarded education as a consumer good, which every one
should enjoy, though very few university graduates return-
ed to the kibbutz. Adler, like Chamberlain, opted for
general education, noting that recently the World Bank
had shifted its preference from vocational education.
However, he cited numerous cases in which limited
vocational education was all that was necessary to
complete the transfer work. By treating education as
an investment and as an input into production, do we not
break down the fundamental economist's distinction between
investment and consumption, confusing education with food,
and other intakes? Shubik explained that this dilemma has
been solved by activity analysis, which provides a simple
distinction between consumption and investment:

> Production activity is an activity which,
> if you raised your income level, you
> would have someone else operate for
> you. Driving, for the most part, is a
> production activity. On the consumption
> side, if you want to go to a play, you go
> to a play; you don't send your butler.

Adler referred to Arthur Lewis' comparisons of
former French and British African territories, which,
together with the evidence from Jamaica, suggested that
some level of education may be essential to economic
activity and therefore treated as investment, but only
at a very modest level that is quickly reached by a
society. He concluded:

> We can resolve the distinction, at least
> on economic rational grounds, between
> education as a consumption good and

education as an investment good by
finding that up to a point, obviously
a level of education is necessary;
beyond that it becomes consumption
and contributes to national welfare,
just as an increase of consumption
does.

Both Shubik and Adler emphasized the need for the
allocation of resources to the lower and secondary
level of schools (e. g. , university education is actually
"overdeveloped" in Chile). Particularly the intermediate
level of education is usually neglected, because support
from the masses urges primary level education, and
intellectuals support university education but the middle
level has no advocates.

EPILOGUE

One cannot declare categorically that the concept
of the transfer of technology will be embraced by the
socio-economic thought, that it is not more than a passing
fad which like so many economic ideas will go out of
fashion. But if the distinguished economists and other
scientists who gathered at Airlie House for three days
are a representative sample, it is fair to say that scarce
intellectual capital can be invested profitably in working
with this concept.

This volume has been designed to provide a theoretical and operational guidance to the transfer of technology;
it is replete with disclaimers that transfer of technology is
a new idea, and that little has been written on the subject.
Contributors can hardly be blamed for interpreting the
concept elastically, and, in a sense, their interpretations
or reactions to the term were sought. The book provides
ample proof of existing polarities, though with many
shadings and overlappings of individual views. A substantial number of scholars see the transfer problem immersed
in a "great, messy background of social, political, and
other factors, " to use Professor Lancaster's tongue-in-
cheek phrase. The other polarity takes a more pragmatic

and operational view of the concept, and, while not unwilling to consider the broader dimensions, tries to delimit
the transfer of technology to the imitation and to the adoption of material and physical artifacts and/or specific
managerial and labor skills.

Splitting on the above central issue usually results
in division on other matters.   Thus, on the vital issue of
choice of technology for transfer, the pragmatists prefer
the latest, advanced technology to other alternatives.   They
depreciate institution-building that allegedly should accompany
or precede new technology, and give priority to vocational
or low-level education rather than to middle or higher
education.   Shock treatment, psychological breaks, and
social discontinuity are valued by the pragmatists, whereas
the soft approach exponents opt for gradual change, pre-
servation of cultural continuity, and gentle handling of the
recipient's "Gestalt. " The latter school is concerned with
welfare functions, income distribution, and the substitution of
increased productivity by the equality of opportunity, and
raises questions: For whom is this transfer of technology?
Who is to benefit from the development? How much
cultural upheaval can be tolerated?

Entrepreneurship as a key to transfer of technology
appears as another side of the dispute.   The lack of indigenous entrepreneurs is lamented and promptly disputed.
Entrepreneurs of extracultural origin are alternately
praised and berated.   Indigenous entrepreneurs are considered very scarce, and drastic measures close to
revolutionary change are necessary to spawn them.
Almost by consensus, the crucial condition for accepting
technology emerges: the encouragement of entrepreneurship in the recipient country.   However, how it can
be accomplished is disputable.   In this respect, the
relevance of Schumpeter's framework is challenged,
as are the lessons of economic history for the modern
transfer of technology, although defenders arise in both
cases.

The operationists brush aside entrepreneurs and
look for direct and immediate levers of transferring technology.   They bring forth numerous proposals for international companies, subcontracting by big firms to

small-scale industries, turn-key plants, a United
Nations University, greater participation of military
organizations, and veterans' extension activities.
Particularly acknowledged is training modelled on
the military programs developed in World War II to
overcome illiteracy, to teach rudimentary skills, and
to provide for the minimum essential economic
activity.

Access to large markets, both domestic and
foreign, is held to be an essential economic condition
to effect technological transfer. Whereas development
of local markets is basically the problem of the recipient country, the acceptance of the products of new
technology by international markets involves policy
decision by the donor countries. Acceptance in foreign
markets of the products of the new technology transferred to underdeveloped countries is related to many
factors, such as the characteristics of the product,
quality control, marketing channels, and the balance-
of-payments position. Information theory and systems
are singled out as particularly important to embryonic
entrepreneurs in developing both domestic and foreign
markets.

On the methodological issues, rigorous theoretical models that center on the linear homogeneous
production function find little favor for the transfer
of technology. Achievements of precision in Kmenta's
chapter at the expense of richness of content are
admired but deplored for the lack of realism. Simulation is proffered as a middle road between content
and precision, but however intriguing, its contribution to the transfer of technology problem has not
been unequivocally established. Moreover, it is
recognized that simulation represents only the final
stage of a step-by-step construction of a statistical
data base that includes study and estimation of partial
relationships and buildup of subsystems and information systems.

This hope for the future use of simulation is
related to the outlines of a strategy for the transfer
of technology that emerges as the end result of this

volume. The focal point of the strategy is a large promotional agency to further the technological transfer. Such an agency would be created specifically for this purpose, or existing organizations with similar functions (such as military organizations, international agencies, or international business firms) may be able to expand their activities to the area of the transfer of technology. Such an agency would attack the problem holistically and realistically with the aid of the information theory, simulation, data banks, and social science centers. Herein lie the future possibilities of work with the concept of the transfer of technology, directing the shock that such transfer creates to speed the process of development.

NOTES

1. Jacob Schmookler, "Technological Change and Economic Theory," American Economic Review, LV (May, 1965), 336.

2. Everett M. Rogers, Diffusion of Innovations (New York: The Free Press of Glencoe, 1962).

3. Daniel L. Spencer and Alexander Woroniak, "The Feasibility of Developing Transfer of Technology Functions," circulated as a background paper at The Airlie House Conference, and published in Kyklos, XX, Fasc. 2 (1967).

4. Daniel L. Spencer, "An External Military Presence, Technological Transfer, and Structural Change." Kyklos, XVIII (1965), 451-74.

5. Jay W. Forrester, "Advertising: A Problem in Industrial Dynamics," Harvard Business Review, XXXVII, No. 2 (March-April, 1959), 100-110; Jay W. Forrester, "Industrial Dynamics-A Major Breakthrough for Decision-Makers," Harvard Business Review, XXXVI, No. 4 (July-August, 1958), 37-66.

6. Meier refers to his strategy of development summarized in the section, "Retrospect and Prospect."